VOL **15** PEA-POL
1231–1318

FUNK & WAGNALLS **new**
ENCYCLOPEDIA
OF SCIENCE

FUNK & WAGNALLS, INC.

HOW TO USE FUNK & WAGNALLS NEW ENCYCLOPEDIA OF SCIENCE

Volumes 1 through 21 have information printed on the front covers, spine, and title pages that make it easy to find the articles you want to read.

- Volume numbers are printed in all three places in Volumes 1 through 21.
- Letter breaks — $\frac{COL}{DIA}$ — are printed in all three places in Volumes 1 through 21. The letters above the line are the first three letters of the first article title in the volume. The letters below the line are the first three letters of the last article title in the volume.
- Page breaks — $\frac{351}{438}$ — are printed on the spines and title pages of Volumes 1 through 21. They provide the page numbers of the first and last text pages in the volume.

Articles are arranged alphabetically by title in Volumes 1 through 21. Most titles are printed in **BOLD-FACE CAPITAL** letters. Some titles are printed in even larger letters.

- Some titles are not article titles, but refer you to the actual article title. Within articles you will find *See* or *See also* other article names for further information. All of these references to other articles are called cross-references.
- Most article titles are followed by a phonetic pronunciation. Use the Pronunciation Guide on page vi of Volume 1 to learn the correct pronunciation of the article title.
- At the end of most articles are two sets of initials. The first set identifies the person who wrote the article. The second set identifies the special consultant who checked the article for accuracy. All of these people are listed by their initials and full names and position on pages v and vi of Volume 1.
- ◾ This symbol at the end of an article indicates that there is a project based on the subject of the article in the Projects, Bibliography & Index volume. The project is found under its article title, and all of the project article titles are arranged alphabetically on pages 1 through 64 of the Projects, Bibliography & Index volume.

The Projects, Bibliography & Index Volume contains three sections. Each is an essential part of the encyclopedia.

- Projects based on articles in the encyclopedia are found in the first section. Each is both entertaining and educational. Each is designed for use by a student and for parental participation if desired.
- Bibliography reading lists in the second section list books under general scientific categories that are also titles of major articles. Each book listed is marked with either a YA (Young Adult) or J (Juvenile) reading level indicator. YA generally applies to readers at the junior high level or higher. J applies to readers at grade levels below junior high school.
- Index entries for all article titles plus many subjects that are not article titles are found in the third section. Instructions on using the Index are found at the start of the Index section in the Projects, Bibliography & Index volume.

PEAR (par) The pear is a tasty, fleshy fruit that grows on a large tree belonging to the rose family. The common pear tree (*Pyrus communis*) reaches a height of 15 m [50 ft] and may live for more than 75 years. It has alternate, oval leaves with toothed margins. (*See* LEAF.) White flowers grow in clusters of as many as 12 blossoms. Each cluster produces one cone-shaped fruit with a smooth skin that may be yellow, red, or brown in color. The pear has a central core with as many as ten seeds. The fruit itself contains many tiny, hardened structures called grit cells. These grit cells give the pear a slightly sandy texture and taste.

More than 95% of the pears produced in the United States are grown along the west coast. Pears are eaten as fresh fruits, or may be canned, dried, or processed into perry, an alcoholic drink. Pears contain little protein and fat, and large amounts of carbohydrates, vitamins, and minerals. Their popularity in the United States is exceeded only by that of the apple and the peach. *See also* ROSE FAMILY.   A.J.C./F.W.S.

PEARL (pərl) The pearl is different from other gems. Most gems are minerals that are mined from beneath the earth. But pearls are formed inside the shells of certain mollusks, especially oysters. Pearls are also different in that they are soft and both absorb and reflect light.

The inner layer of a mollusk shell consists of a very smooth and shiny material called nacre or mother-of-pearl. The substance is a form of calcium carbonate. It is secreted (pro-

A worker at Mikimoto Pearl Company, Japan, seeding an oyster with nacre. © Travelpix/FPG International

duced) by the outer skin of the animal. This outer skin is called a mantle. Grains of sand and other foreign bodies often get inside the shell and cause irritation. The animal then responds by secreting more nacre around the object and forming a little ball. This ball is the pearl. Several kinds of mollusks make pearls in this way, but the best pearls come from the pearl oyster. Pearl formation in these animals is usually triggered by a tiny parasitic worm which burrows into the mantle.

The pearl has the same luster and color as the lining of the shell of the mollusk. But few pearl-forming mollusks produce the nacre that is necessary for valuable pearls. Valuable pearls come from a few species of oysters found in tropical seas.

Pearl oysters are collected by divers in some parts of the Pacific. Natural pearls are very valuable for use in jewelry. But most of the pearls seen today are cultured pearls. These are obtained by placing little pieces of nacre inside the oysters and waiting for the pearls to grow. When the oyster is seven years old, its shell is opened. There is a valuable pearl in about one out of every twenty such oysters opened. *See also* OYSTER.

J.J.A./C.S.H.

PEAT (pēt) Peat is partially decayed plant matter that has collected in marshes and swamps over a long period of time. It is generally the first stage in the formation of coal. Dried peat is used mainly for fuel in places where coal and oil are scarce. Dried peat varies from a light yellow-brown substance resembling tangled hay to deeper layers of dark brown resembling brown coal.

Peat forms in layers. The upper layers contain the remains of plants, herbs, and moss that rotted and dried in the shallow, acid water of the marsh or swamp. The layers are compressed by the weight of the water and each other. The lower layers contain about 90 percent water and look like mud when first removed.

Peat is found throughout the world. The Soviet Union, Canada, and Finland have the largest deposits. In the United States the largest deposits of peat are in Minnesota. The Dismal Swamp in Virgina also has peat bogs (swamps). Workers dig and stack peat by hand in Ireland and some other countries. Large machines are used for this work in the Soviet Union and other European countries.

The peat is dried by simply exposing it to the air for a period of time. Dried peat is used as fuel to heat houses in Ireland. In the Soviet Union, it is even used as fuel in some electric power plants. Black peat is used as a fertilizer. Fluffy, brown peat is used as a packing material. *See also* COAL.   W.R.P./R.J.B.

Stacks of drying peat in the Netherlands are shown above. In the background, workers are cutting peat which will be dried and used for fuel.

PECCARY (pek′ ə rē) The peccary is a piglike mammal that lives in the forests and desert scrublands of Central and South America and the southwestern United States. Peccaries make up the family Tayassuidae, and are distantly related to the true pigs (the family Suidae).

There are three species of peccaries: (1) the collared peccary, or javelina, which lives in South America and the United States; (2) the white-lipped peccary, which is found in Central and South America; and (3) the tagua, or Chacoan peccary, which lives in Paraguay, Bolivia, and Argentina.

Peccaries look like slender, active hogs. They can grow 76 cm [30 in] tall and are covered with coarse, grizzled, blackish gray fur. Peccaries are rooting animals. They eat roots and plants. They live in herds, which can range in size from a few peccaries to several hundred. Peccaries are shy animals, but fight viciously when cornered. The jaguar is their most dangerous natural enemy. Peccaries are hunted by man for their skin, which is used to make pigskin jackets and gloves.

W.R.P./J.J.M.

PECTIN (pek' tən) Pectin is a white substance found in the walls of many fruit and vegetable cells. It is a complex carbohydrate made up of sugar molecules. Pectin is one of the main reasons why jelly can be made from certain fruits.

The amount of pectin in fruit depends upon the ripeness and kind of fruit. Some fruits are high in pectin. These include apples, blackberries, cranberries, gooseberries, loganberries, grapes, currants, crab apples, and plums. When these fruits are boiled in water, the pectins form a jellylike mass that is used to make jams and jellies.

Commercial pectins, which are made by concentrating certain fruit juices, are added to fruits that are low in pectin. Peaches, pineapples, and strawberries, for example, are low in natural pectin. Artificial pectins must be added to these fruits to make jellies or jams.

W.R.P./M.H.S.

PECTORALIS MAJOR (pek' tə ral' əs mā'jər) The pectoralis major is the large muscle that covers most of the front of the chest. It originates at the ribs, sternum (breastbone), and clavicle (collarbone). The pectoralis major extends across the chest and is attached by a tendon to the humerus (the bone of the upper arm). The muscle is responsible for many of the arm's movements. It can pull the arm toward the side of the body, or swing it forward in front of the chest.

The pectoralis minor is a smaller muscle that is underneath the pectoralis major. It originates at the ribs and is attached to the scapula (shoulder blade). This muscle is used to move the shoulder forward and downward. *See also* MUSCLE.

D.M.H.W./J.J.F.

PEGASUS (peg' ə səs) Pegasus is a constellation visible from the mid-northern hemisphere between August and December. Three stars of Pegasus and one star from the adjacent constellation Andromeda form the Great Square of Pegasus. One side of the Great Square can be used as pointer stars to locate the North Star.

According to ancient Greek mythology, Pegasus was a winged horse placed in the heavens by the god Zeus. *See also* CONSTELLATION.

J.M.C./C.R.

PEKING MAN (pē' king' man') Peking man was a prehistoric human being whose remains were found in northern China. He probably lived about 350,000 years ago during the Pleistocene epoch. He is classified as *Homo erectus*.

Peking man was about 155 cm (61 in) tall. He had a flat skull with a brain capacity somewhat less than that of modern people. Peking man had a chinless jaw, small forehead, and humanlike teeth. His arm and leg bones were remarkably similar to those of people today.

Peking man was first identified as a prehistoric human by Davidson Black in 1927. The numerous tools and charred deer bones found near the discovery sites indicate that Peking man was a hunter who used fire. Many of Peking man's fossils were lost while being taken out of China in 1941. *See also* HUMAN BEING; PLEISTOCENE EPOCH.

J.M.C./S.O.

PELICAN (pel' i kən) A pelican is a large bird that belongs to the family Pelecanidae. There are six species in the world, but only two species—the white and brown pelicans—live in North America. The brown

Pelicans are large, fish-eating water birds with enormous pouched beaks. The pouches are not used to carry their catch, but some species use them as fishing nets. Pelicans feed their young by passing partly digested food back into the pouch. The young pelicans reach their heads into their parents' pouches to get the food.

pelican lives along the seashores of western and southeastern North America. The white pelican winters in those areas, but it also nests beside freshwater lakes of western and central North America.

Pelicans grow about 112 cm [45 in] long. They have webbed feet, a long neck, and a long, broad bill which is used to catch fish, the pelican's main food. Brown pelicans often dive from heights of 10m [33 ft] into the water to catch fish. Perhaps one of the best-known features of pelicans is the pouch under their

bills. The pouch looks like a big bag when the bird inflates it. Many people think that it is used only to store fish. But scientists have learned that it is also used to help the pelicans remain cool. It works like the radiator on a car.   S.R.G./L.L.S.

PELVIS (pel'vəs) The pelvis is a structure made of several bones that are fused together to support the lower abdomen and to protect the internal structures. The pelvis has two halves called innominate bones. Each innominate bone is made up of three smaller bones: the ilium, ischium, and pubis. The innominate bones are fused in front and in back. (*See* VERTEBRAE.) The ilium is the flat, blade-shaped bone that can be felt as the bone at the hip. The ischium supports the weight of the upper body when a person is sitting. The pubis forms an arch in front.

The backbone rises from the top of the pelvis. The femurs (thighbones) are connected to the lower pelvis by ball-and-socket joints. (*See* FEMUR.) These joints are very strong because they must support the weight of the upper part of the body when a person stands. There are many large, strong muscles leading from the pelvis to each femur.

A woman's pelvis is broader and more flared than a man's. This provides extra support for the uterus and the unborn baby during pregnancy. The central cavity of the pelvis is also larger in the woman so that the baby can pass through it during birth. *See also* BONE; JOINT. A.J.C./J.J.F.

PENDULUM (pen′ jə ləm) A pendulum is a body that hangs from a fixed point and is free to swing. A simple pendulum consists of a heavy mass called a bob on the end of a lightweight cord or rod. If the cord or rod is not light, the pendulum is called a compound pendulum.

If a pendulum is held to one side and released, it swings down to the vertical (straight up-and-down) position. It continues moving away from the vertical and slows down until it stops. It then returns back through the vertical. It stops when it reaches the point at which it was released. The cycle then starts again. This movement of the pendulum is called oscillation. (*See* OSCILLATION.) The time it takes to complete one full

The pendulum swings to-and-fro at a constant rate, making it a good regulator for clocks. The period of each swing depends only on the length of the pendulum.

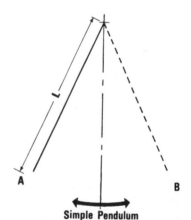

Simple Pendulum
Period of oscillation T is the time taken to swing from extreme position A to extreme position B and back to A

$$T = 2\pi\sqrt{\frac{L}{g}}$$

L = distance from point of suspension to center of gravity of bob

g = acceleration due to gravity

cycle is called the period of oscillation. For small oscillations, the period depends only on the length of the rod or cord. It does not depend on the mass of the bob. Nor does it depend on the angle through which the pendulum swings. The time that it takes for a pendulum to complete each swing is the same. Because of this, pendulums are used for timing in clocks. Christian Huygens, a Dutch scientist, invented the first clock with a pendulum in 1657. *See also* FOUCAULT PENDULUM. M.E./R.W.L.

PENGUIN (pen′ gwən) Penguins are 18 species of seabirds that belong to the order Sphenisciformes. Their wings have evolved into flippers. As a result, they cannot fly, but they are excellent swimmers. All penguins live in the southern hemisphere, mostly at the edge of Antarctica. Penguin colonies, or rookeries, are found where there are cold water currents, as far north as the Galapagos Islands, a group of Pacific Ocean islands near the equator. A single rookery may contain more than a million penguins.

All penguins walk in an upright position. Because they have stout bodies and such short legs, they walk with a waddling motion. A penguin's body is covered with a thick layer of short feathers which are white on the bird's belly and black or dark blue on its back. These feathers are waterproof and have tiny air spaces that help keep the bird warm. Penguins spend much of their time in icy waters, swimming or looking for food. Their diet consists mostly of fish and squid.

The emperor penguin (*Aptenodytes forsteri*) is the largest living penguin. It is about 1.2 m [4 ft] tall. *See also* BIRD.

A.J.C./L.L.S.

PENICILLIN (pen′ ə sil′ ən) Penicillin is a powerful germicide, or germ killer. It is made by molds belonging to the genus *Penicillium*. Penicillin was discovered in 1928 by Alexander Fleming. In 1940, Howard Florey and

Penguins (facing right) are flightless birds whose wings have evolved into flippers, making them excellent swimmers.

Ernst Chain purified penicillin for use in medicine. The drug was so effective it caused an interest which led to the development of many drugs known as antibiotics. (*See* ANTIBIOTIC.)

At first, penicillin could be made only in small amounts by growing the mold *Penicillium notatum* on culture fluid or in broth in bottles or pans. But the yield of penicillin was very small. Later, a deep culture method was developed. In this method, large amounts of the mold were grown in tanks. Soon, better strains of *Penicillium* were found. The strains

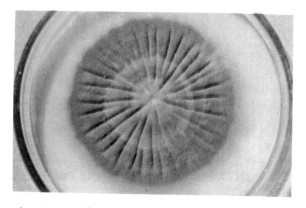

A colony of *Penicillium* mold (above) growing on agar jelly in a petri dish is shown. Penicillin is extracted from large quantities of such molds.

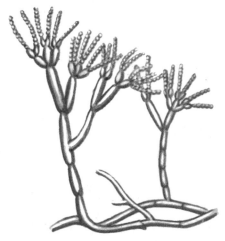

A magnified part of a *Penicillium* mold colony shows the spores which reproduce the mold.

used by manufacturers produce almost 5,000 times as much penicillin as those first used by researchers. Hundreds of tons of penicillin are made every year in the United States.

Not all harmful germs are destroyed by penicillin. However, most of the bacteria that cause common infections, such as those of the blood, are very sensitive to penicillin.

Penicillin is the least poisonous antibiotic available, although a few people are allergic to it. For these people, even a tiny amount of the drug can cause great discomfort. Some people would die if penicillin were injected into their bodies.

Most bacteria are resistant—they can grow even when an antibiotic is present. For instance, the proper dosage of penicillin will kill most bacteria. But one type of bacteria, the staphylococcus, has many strains that naturally resist penicillin. *See also* CHAIN, ERNST; FLEMING, SIR ALEXANDER; FLOREY, J.J.A./J.J.F.

PENNSYLVANIAN PERIOD (pen′ səl vā′ nyən pir′ ē əd) The Pennsylvanian period is the division of the Paleozoic era that began about 325 million years ago. It lasted about 45 million years and is the second half of the Carboniferous period.

In North America today, rocks of the Pennsylvanian period contain vast amounts of coal, natural gas, and petroleum.

During the Pennsylvanian period, forests of huge ferns grew in the swampy soil. Hundreds of insect species, including giant roaches, thrived at this time. Amphibians and sea life flourished. Reptiles made their first appearance during the Pennsylvanian period. *See also* CARBONIFEROUS PERIOD; COAL; PALEOZOIC ERA. J.M.C./W.R.S.

PEONY (pē′ ə nē) The peony is a herbaceous plant with large, handsome flowers. It is a member of the crowfoot or buttercup family, Ranunculaceae. In early spring, peonies have shrubby or herblike stems. The cluster of leafy shoots—red and bright green in appearance—creates a striking effect a few weeks before the flowers appear in late spring or early summer. The blossoms are usually white, pink, or red. Peonies grow 90 to 120 cm [3 to 4 ft] high. They are found throughout the world.

Many of the cultivated peonies found in the United States are offsprings of two species—the common peony of southern Europe and the Chinese peony. The large flowers of the common peony are red and crimson. Peonies are hardy plants that live a long time. W.R.P./M.H.S.

PEPPER FAMILY The pepper (pep′ ər) family (Piperaceae) includes 10 genera (plural of genus) with more than 1,500 species of dicotyledonous flowering plants. The family includes herbaceous plants, shrubs, vines, and trees, most of which grow in tropical areas. They have alternate, simple leaves. The flowers do not have sepals or petals. They grow in dense spikes. (*See* INFLORESCENCE.) Most of the plants are monoecious, with both male flowers and female flowers on the same plant.

The most important member of the pepper family is the black pepper plant, *Piper nigrum*. It is a perennial climbing plant that produces aerial roots. It may reach a length of 10 m [33 ft]. It produces small, berrylike peppercorns which turn from green to red as they mature. The peppercorns are usually harvested at maturity, cleaned, and dried. The peppercorns become black as they dry. They can then be ground, sifted, and sold as the spice called black pepper. White pepper comes from the same plant, but the husk is removed from the peppercorn before it is ground.

Red pepper and garden peppers come from plants belonging to genus *Capsicum* of the nightshade family. (*See* NIGHTSHADE

FAMILY.) They are not related to the pepper family. A.J.C./M.H.S.

PERCENTAGE (pər sent' ij) Percentage is a rate or proportion per hundred. It comes from the Latin phrase *per centum,* meaning "by the hundred." "Thirty percent of the students at this school are wearing red sweaters" means that out of every 100 students in the school, 30 of them are wearing red sweaters. In other words, 30 hundredths of the students are wearing red sweaters. Hundredths may be expressed as common fractions, such as 30/100; as decimal fractions, 0.30; or as percent, 30%. Each of these figures represents 30 parts of a whole that has 100 parts.

Numbers greater than a whole (100/100) can be expressed as percentages. To say something has increased to 300% means it is 3 times as large as it was.

To change a decimal fraction to a percent, the decimal fraction is multiplied by 100. This is done by moving the decimal point two places to the right and adding the percent sign. For example, .25 = 25%, .50 = 50%, and .4782 = 47.82%. To change a common fraction to a percent, the common fraction is first changed to a decimal fraction. For example, 1/10 = .10 = 10%.

Such operations can be reversed. For example, 50% = .50 = ½. The percent is divided by 100 by moving the decimal point two places to the left and dropping the percent sign. The decimal fraction may then be changed to a common fraction.

Percentages are used in everyday life. Bankers use percentages to figure interests on savings and loans accounts. In baseball, team standings and batting averages are based on percentages. Scientists often show the results of their observations and experiments with percentages. J.J.A./S.P.A.

PERCEPTION (pər sep' shən) Perception is the process by which a person or animal makes sense out of the area around it. The world consists of various kinds of physical energy. Knowledge of the world comes through the sense organs. For example, the ears sense certain types of mechanical vibrations (sound) in the air. The eyes sense certain wavelengths of electromagnetic energy (light).

The sense organs change the various kinds of energy into nerve impulses. These impulses go to the brain. Through the process of perception, the patterns of energies become known as objects and events. But the process of perception does not reveal objects and events. For instance, human beings see color, but there is no light or color as we know it in the waves that stimulate the eyes. The brain organizes and interprets nervous impulses from the eyes as light and color. Together, the sense organs and the brain transform physical energy into information.

There are three different levels of perception. Detection is concerned with whether a person can sense that he or she is being stimulated by some form of energy. For example, a sound may be so slight that he or she can hardly hear it. Recognition is being able to identify a particular pattern of stimulation, such as being able to tell that a particular sound is a tone from a piano. Discrimination is being able to perceive patterns of stimulation as different, such as differences between two similar musical tones. *See also* COLOR; EAR; EYE; NERVOUS SYSTEM; OPTICAL ILLUSION; PSYCHOLOGY; SENSES. J.J.A./J.J.F.

PERCH (pərch') A perch is a freshwater fish that belongs to the family Percidae. North American fish included in the perch family are the darters, walleye pike, and yellow perch. (*See* DARTER; WALLEYE PIKE.) The yellow perch is very common in lakes and rivers throughout North America. It is frequently referred to just as a perch. The yellow perch ranges between 18 and 40 cm [7 to 16 in] in length. Its body is green along the top and back, yellowish on the belly, and has orange stripes on the sides. The yellow perch is a popular game and food fish.

Many other fish are called perch, but none of them are true perch. For example, the white perch is actually a bass. (*See* BASS.) There is a family of saltwater fish in North America known as the surfperches.   S.R.G./E.C.M.

PERCHING BIRD (pərch′ ing bərd′)

Perching birds, or passerine birds, belong to the order Passeriformes. A perching bird has feet that are able to grip a twig or branch in much the same way that a human hand would grasp a branch. The feet of the bird have three toes in front and one toe in back.

Nearly half of all known birds are perching birds. These include all of the songbirds, flycatchers, swallows, crows, warblers, finches, blackbirds, and many more. *See also* BIRD; BLACKBIRD; CROW; FINCH; SWALLOW; WARBLER.   S.R.G./L.L.S.

PERENNIAL PLANT (pə ren′ ē əl plant′)

A perennial plant is any plant that lives for more than two years. All woody plants, and some herbaceous plants, are perennials. (*See* HERBACEOUS PLANT; WOODY PLANT.) Most herbaceous perennial plants, such as asparagus, have perennial roots. The aboveground structures (stems, leaves, flowers) die off every year. Some plants that are perennial in one climate may be annual in another. *See also* ANNUAL PLANT; BIENNIAL PLANT; MONOCARPIC PLANT.   A.J.C./M.H.S.

PERIANTH (per′ ē anth′)

The perianth is the calyx and the corolla of a flower. The calyx is made up of the sepals, which are petallike structures around the base of the flower. The corolla is made up of the petals. Sometimes, either the sepals or the petals, or both, may be missing. In some plants, such as the grasses, the perianth is reduced to two scalelike lodicules. (*See* GRASS.) *See also* FLOWER.   A.J.C./M.H.S.

PERIODIC MOTION (pir′ ē äd′ ik mō′ shən)

Periodic motion is any motion that repeats itself in a regular way. The pendulum is a good example of periodic motion. The pendulum is said to oscillate, or swing back and forth, about its vertical, or resting, position. The time taken for the pendulum to make one complete cycle is called the period of motion.

Other examples of periodic motion are the pistons in an automobile engine, the balance wheel of a watch, the vibration of a piano or violin string, and the human pulse. Galileo is said to have used his pulse as a timing device in his studies of the motion of falling bodies. *See also* GALILEO; OSCILLATION; PENDULUM.   M.E./R.W.L.

PERIODIC TABLE *See* ELEMENT.

PERISCOPE (per′ ə skōp′)

A periscope is an optical instrument with which a person can see around corners and other obstructions. Some periscopes also have a magnifying feature that makes distant objects appear to be closer. A periscope is somewhat similar to a telescope. Basically, it consists of a long tube with a reflecting mirror or prism at each end. The reflecting surfaces are parallel to one another. They are arranged at an angle of 45 degrees inside the tube.

Periscopes are important instruments in submarines and tanks. Officers aboard a submerged submarine can see events on the surface by looking through a periscope. A submarine's periscope can move up and down and turn to look in a complete circle. Submarines often cruise at what is called periscope depth with only the top of the periscope showing above the surface of the water. Periscopes also allow tank commanders to view battlefield events from inside their armored vehicles.

Periscopes have other uses, too. Simple periscopes made of cardboard are used by some people in large crowds at parades and sporting events. They help the users see over the heads of the people in front of them. Periscopes are also used in industry to observe nuclear reactions and the interiors of special furnaces and other dangerous devices. The longest periscope in the world measures 27 m [90 ft]. Located at the National Reactor Testing Station in Idaho Falls, Idaho, it is used to view details of the operation of nuclear reactors. *See also* TELESCOPE.   W.R.P./S.S.B.

Using a periscope, the commander of a U.S. Navy nuclear-powered submarine surveys the surface.

PERISTALSIS (per' ə stȯl' səs) Peristalsis is a special kind of muscle movement that happens in the alimentary canal. The muscles in the walls of the gullet (esophagus) and intestine squeeze food along in the proper direction. This squeezing movement is called peristalsis. There are long muscles and circular muscles that work together to make waves of movement. The muscles, controlled from the spinal cord, are smooth. We do not have voluntary control of them and most of the time we are not aware of their action. *See also* ALIMENTARY CANAL; DIGESTION.

C.M./J.J.F.

PERMIAN PERIOD (pər' mē ən pir' ē əd) The Permian period, or last division of the Paleozoic era, began about 280 million years ago and lasted about 55 million years.

At the beginning of the Permian period, the southern continents were mostly covered with ice. At the same time, the climate of northern continents remained warm and dry. Significant effects of continental drift are thought to have occurred during the Permian period. (*See* CONTINENTAL DRIFT.)

Conifers, the first seed plants, appeared at this time. Fish, amphibians, and reptiles flourished. There were many ammonites and brachiopods, while trilobites died out.

Sedimentary rock containing copper formed during this time in parts of Texas, Oklahoma and Germany. Great folding also occurred at this time during the formation of the Ural Mountains in western Russia and Appalachian Mountains in the eastern United States. *See also* FOLDING; PALEOZOIC ERA.

J.M.C./W.R.S.

This is part of the Shenandoah Valley, which was formed during the Permian period.

PERPETUAL MOTION (pər pech′ wəl mō′ shən) Perpetual motion is motion that goes on forever. Throughout history, people have tried to build perpetual motion machines. These machines were supposed to operate indefinitely, but all the attempts failed. By the 1850s, scientists had discovered two very important laws of physics: the first and second laws of thermodynamics. (*See* THERMODYNAMICS.)

The first law says that energy can be neither created nor destroyed. This law is also called the law of conservation of energy. A perpetual motion machine that attempts to break this law is called a perpetual motion machine of the first kind. One example consists of a wheel with spokes. Each spoke has a ball that can move along it between the rim and the hub. When the spoke is near the bottom of the wheel, the ball can fall to the rim (outside of the wheel). As the wheel keeps turning, the ball should fall back to the hub (middle of the wheel). When the wheel moves round a little more, the ball should fall back to the rim again. The force of it hitting the rim is supposed to keep the wheel turning. However, the ball loses energy as it hits the rim and friction occurs with the spoke. The wheel soon stops.

Machines that do not work because they break the second law of thermodynamics are called perpetual motion machines of the second kind. This second law states that heat cannot flow from a colder body to a hotter one without adding more energy than is produced. Machines that attempt to turn heat into other forms of energy with complete efficiency violate this law. (*See* EFFICIENCY.)

Recently, experiments in superconductivity have come close to perpetual motion. In superconductivity, certain substances lose their electrical resistance at very low temperatures. This means that an electric current can flow through the substance forever. However, energy is needed to keep the substance cold. (*See* SUPERCONDUCTIVITY.)   M.E./J.T.

The medieval perpetual motion machine (above) did not provide perpetual motion because friction between the various parts eventually prevented the screw from conveying water to the tank.

PERSEUS (pər′ süs′) Perseus is a constellation that lies betwen Cassiopeia and Taurus. It is visible from the mid-northern hemisphere between October and March. Perseus contains the variable star Algol. According to Greek myths, Perseus killed the Gorgon Medusa. *See also* CONSTELLATION; VARIABLE STAR.   J.M.C./C.R.

PERSPECTIVE (pər spek′ tive) Perspective is a way of showing a solid (three-dimensional) object on paper. A solid object has three dimensions: length, width, and depth. A surface, such as the top of a piece of paper, has only two dimensions. The third dimension of an object is represented by perspective. Any object appears to become smaller as we move away from it. This is called linear perspective. For example, the further side of a cube seems smaller than the nearer side. The two lines that join the two sides do not seem parallel. They are said to converge (come together) to a point on the horizon. This point is called the vanishing point.   M.E./S.S.B.

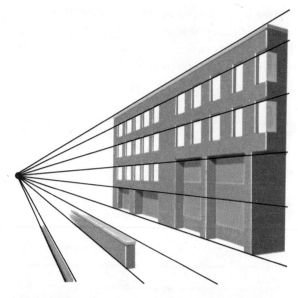

A perspective drawing is one in which everything appears at the size it would be if viewed in depth by an observer. A simple perspective drawing of a building is shown here. To give the impression of depth, the artist selects a point on the horizon where the lines of the building converge—this is called the vanishing point. If the artist added other buildings to the drawing, they too would have lines that converge on the horizon, but the vanishing points would be different.

PESTICIDE (pes′ tə sīd′) A pesticide is a chemical that is used to kill pests. Some pests spread disease. Others eat or otherwise damage crops and other desirable plants. Some pests are parasites that damage livestock, pets, and human beings. A pest may be an animal, plant, protozoan, fungus, bacterium, alga, or virus. In the past, poisons were used to control pests, but these poisons often affected other organisms as well. Scientists are constantly working on new chemicals which will affect only the target organism—the pest.

Different chemicals are used for different kinds of pests. For example, herbicides kill weeds, fungicides kill fungi, and insecticides kill insects. Rats and other harmful rodents are often controlled with anticoagulants. Anticoagulants are chemicals that keep the blood from clotting so that the animal will bleed to death from even the tiniest scratch. Some animals are brought into traps because they are attracted to special chemicals called pheromones. (*See* PHEROMONE.)

In many cases, a pest becomes resistant to a certain pesticide after repeated exposure. (*See* IMMUNITY.) When this happens, the pest population increases rapidly, often becoming a greater problem than before. Pesticides pollute the environment, killing valuable animal life, such as honeybees and fish. And they are taken up by the food chain, eventually finding their way into the food we eat. Because of all the problems associated with the use of chemical pesticides, many scientists prefer biological control. In biological control, a pest is kept under control by its natural enemies. (*See* BIOLOGICAL CONTROL.) *See also* CONSERVATION; FUNGICIDE; HERBICIDE; INSECTICIDE; POLLUTION.   A.J.C./R.J.B.

Air from soil fumigated with methyl bromide pesticide is tested for chemical residue. Some pesticides, such as DDT, can harm animals because the pesticide does not break down in the soil.

An airplane is shown spraying a cotton field with pesticides to destroy insect pests.

In an African town, a United Nations helicopter is shown spraying a pesticide over vegetation to kill malaria-carrying mosquitoes.

petrels have tubelike nostrils on the top of the beak. Petrels eat fish, shrimp, and plankton. Storm petrels often follow ships at sea, eating wastes that are thrown overboard. *See also* BIRD; PLANKTON. S.R.G./L.L.S.

A petrel is pictured above. Petrels are seabirds which have tubelike nostrils on top of their beaks. They are long-winged, strong-flying birds. Ten species of petrels are found off the coasts of North America.

PETAL (pet′ əl) The petal is the part of a flower that is usually brightly colored and leaflike in shape. Its main function is to attract insects and birds to the flower for pollination. (*See* POLLINATION.) Most monocotyledons have petals in multiples of three. (*See* MONOCOTYLEDON.) Most dicotyledons have petals in multiples of four or five (*See* DICOTYLEDON.) Sometimes, the petals may be fused to form a cup or tubelike corolla. *See also* FLOWER; MIMICRY. A.J.C./M.H.S.

PETREL (pe′ trəl) Petrels are small seabirds that belong to the families Procellariidae and Hydrobatidae. There are ten species of petrels found off the coasts of North America. Three species belong to the family Procellariidae and are called large, or gadfly, petrels. The other seven belong to the family Hydrobatidae and are called storm petrels. The storm petrels are much smaller than the gadfly petrels.

Petrels are long-winged, strong-flying birds. They are usually brown and white. All

PETRIFIED FOREST (pe′ trə fīd fȯr′ əst) A petrified forest is a forest that has changed to stone. The petrification process usually begins when plants are rapidly buried by volcanic ash, mud, or sand. Water containing minerals seeps through the debris into the buried plants. There, the silica or calcium carbonate in the water replaces the decaying plant cells. The result is an exact duplicate of the original plant. Petrified plants sometimes represent unique species that flourished on earth for a very short period of time.

In a petrified forest, the trees are no longer standing. Instead, many petrified logs lie in scattered positions. They have been stripped of their stone covering by erosion. The Petrified Forest National Park in Arizona contains the largest and most colorful collection of petrified plants in the world. The trees probably grew about 150 million years ago. Other petrified forests in the United States are found in New York and Wyoming. *See also* PALEOBOTANY. J.M.C./W.R.S.

PETROLEUM

Petroleum (pə trō′ lē əm) is a thick, black liquid found usually in pools beneath the earth's surface. It is one of the most valuable substances found in the earth's crust and is a mixture of useful oils from which gasoline, fuel oils, and lubricating oils are produced. Petroleum is sometimes called ''black gold'' because it is so valuable to human beings. The petroleum industry also uses petroleum to make a wide range of products, including plastics, paint, drugs, explosives, cleaning fluids, and detergents.

Formation of petroleum The word ''petroleum,'' meaning ''rock oil,'' comes from the Greek. Most scientists believe that petroleum is the decayed remains of tiny animals and plants that lived in shallow seas millions of years ago. These remains were buried in clays or silt brought down by rivers and decomposed into simple hydrocarbons by bacteria in the absence of air. Eventually, the clays or silt were buried and enclosed by permeable rocks (porous rocks through which liquids can flow). The most common permeable rocks are sandstones and limestones. As the clays or silt were buried under other rocks, they were pressed together by pressure into shale. The simple compounds were changed by pressure into long-chain hydrocarbon oils. (*See* POLYMERIZATION; SHALE.) The oil was squeezed out of the shales and flowed into the permeable rocks. Experts believe that the differences between one kind of petroleum and another come from differences in temperature, pressure, and other conditions, instead of differences in the living creatures from which they were formed.

Where petroleum is found For petroleum to be extracted (removed), it must have collected in adequate reservoirs (amounts) in the earth's crust. Also, the permeable rocks in which it collected must have been sealed to prevent the petroleum from leaking away. Oil floats on water, and, usually, collects in structures that are sealed on top. The impermeable cap rock that seals an underground reservoir of petroleum is usually shale or rock salt. (*See* ROCK SALT.)

The most common reservoir is an anticline, or upfold of rocks that forms an underground dome or ridge. (*See* ANTICLINE.) Another structure, important in the Gulf of Mexico, is a salt dome. Salt domes are bodies of salt that have been forced up, breaking apart and tilting the lower layers of rock and raising those above it into a dome. Petroleum collects in the rocks above the salt dome and also in the upturned rocks on its side—being, in this case, held there by the salt.

A test oil well, drilled during a petroleum survey in Nova Scotia, Canada, is pictured above.

An offshore oil rig is pictured above. The rocks beneath the seabed are an increasingly important source of petroleum.

Drill bits used to drill for petroleum have to be very hard. Note the difference between the old, worn bit (left) and the new bit (right).

Another type of reservoir can occur when rocks are tilted and then faulted, so that an impermeable shale or other kind of rock is brought next to the permeable one. (*See* FAULT.) In this way, the oil is sealed on the underside of the fault. Sometimes, a lens-shaped body of sandstone or limestone may act as a reservoir. (*See* LIMESTONE; SANDSTONE.)

Prospecting for petroleum Possible reservoirs containing petroleum are found by geologists and geophysicists. (*See* GEOPHYSICS.) Geologists study surface rocks and map their findings. This increases their knowledge about the structures beneath the ground. The structures can be measured more accurately by geophysicists who use the principles of seismology. (*See* SEISMOLOGY.) Siesmological methods involve making small explosions in the ground and measuring the shock waves that pass through the earth's crust. The shock waves are deflected at boundaries between different types of rock. The type and structure of the rock can be established by noting the time the shock waves take to travel to various places around the explosion.

Another method involves measuring the force of gravity at various places. For example, when a salt dome lies beneath the earth's surface, the force of gravity at the surface is slightly reduced. Other prospecting methods involve the use of electricity or magnetism. (*See* ELECTRICITY; MAGNETISM.) Geophysicists can establish only that a reservoir of petroleum may exist. The only way to find out whether the reservoir actually contains petroleum is to drill a hole.

Extracting petroleum Early uses for petroleum included lighting, treating roads, waterproofing, and medicine. People used oils that leaked naturally out of the surface of the earth. Later, they drilled shallow holes by hand. The first mechanical drilling for oil was done by Edwin Drake in Pennsylvania in 1859. He used a steam engine. Early drilling was done by percussion (breaking up the rock by hammering).

Much drilling is performed with a rotating (turning) shaft. Different types of bits (the drilling mechanism at the end of the shaft) are used depending on the hardness of the rock. (*See* DRILLING.) The bits break the rocks to fragments which are washed out with water and a soft clay called bentonite. The bentonite also seals the walls of the hole and keeps the drilling bit cool. When geologists want to study the rocks being drilled, a coring bit is used. Coring bits have diamonds around the edges to cut through the rock. They also have a hollow center to hold the core. The core is removed occasionally for examination.

In the Middle East, long pipelines are used to carry crude oil from the wells across the desert to ports where it can be shipped.

An oil tanker is shown alongside a jetty at an oil refinery in South Wales. Some tankers weigh more than 450,000 metric tons [500,000 tons].

Usually, petroleum is found floating on salty water. Often a layer of natural gas is found on top of the petroleum. This natural gas consists mostly of methane. (*See* METHANE.) Often, it is the only useful substance obtained from drilling. Petroleum may be absent or nearly so.

If the reservoir is under great pressure, the gases may be dissolved in the petroleum and may come out with it. When the drilling reaches the reservoir, the petroleum may come out under pressure in a gusher. Gushers are prevented whenever possible because they are wasteful and cause pollution.

When the pressure falls, petroleum is pumped out of the reservoir. The final stage is to flush out any remaining oil with water. Still, one fifth to more than one half of the petroleum is left behind, clinging to the walls of small holes in the rock. The amount wasted depends on the size of the holes. The smaller the hole, the more petroleum is lost. Since World War II, offshore drilling, or drilling below the ocean floor off the coast, has proved very productive. Most offshore drilling is done in the Pacific Ocean off the coast of California and in the Gulf of Mexico off the

coasts of Louisiana and Texas.

After the petroleum has been taken out, it is taken by pipeline, trucks, rail, or tankers to a refinery. There, the petroleum is separated and changed into a number of useful products.

Chemistry of petroleum The oils in petroleum are compounds of carbon and hydrogen with small amounts of oxygen, nitrogen, and sulfur. The main compounds of petroleum are paraffins. (*See* PARAFFIN.) These compounds have carbon atoms joined into chains by single bonds. In some parts of the world, petroleum has a large proportion of naphthenes, with the carbon atoms arranged in rings. The unit is a ring of six carbon atoms with three of them joined by two bonds instead of one. (*See* BENZENE; ORGANIC CHEMISTRY.) Petroleum usually has small amounts of olefins. Olefins are like the paraffins except that some of the carbon atoms have two bonds between them and, therefore, fewer hydrogen atoms. (*See* OLEFIN.)

Refining petroleum Petroleum is first heated (distilled) in a furnace and the gases are passed into a chimney called a fractionating column. The column is hottest at the bottom and gets cooler toward the top. The boiling point and density of the several compounds in the petroleum depend mainly on the weight of their molecules. This is largely the result of the number of carbon atoms in them. When petroleum boils, the lighter substances travel up the fractionating column before condensing again into a liquid. (*See* CONDENSATION.) The various fractions (various oils and other materials) are collected in vessels called bubble cap trays placed at intervals up the column. The lightest fractions supply gasoline. Increasingly heavy fractions give kerosene and fuel oil. The fuel oil cannot be separated simply by boiling in air, so residue is reheated in a vacuum where the fractions boil at a much lower temperature. This further boiling yields diesel oil, lubricating oil, asphalt, and paraffin wax.

The chief use of petroleum today is as

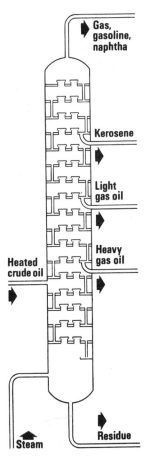

Crude oil is distilled with steam in a fractionating tower (left). Six main fractions are distilled. A section (below) of the tower shows "bubble caps" which trap and condense rising petroleum vapors carried by steam (red arrows). Bubble caps at various levels are connected, which allows the petroleum liquids to drain downward or reflux (black arrows).

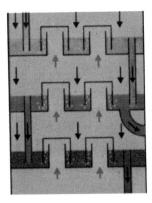

gasoline or diesel oil for engines. Crude oil (raw petroleum) does not yield enough of these lighter fractions. To increase the supply, the heavier fractions are broken down into lighter ones by cracking. Cracking is performed by heating the heavier fractions under pressure, sometimes using a catalyst. (*See* CATALYST; CRACKING.) In this process, some olefins are formed. This improves the quality of the gasoline which is measured by octane rating. (*See* OCTANE RATING.) The gasoline obtained originally is also put through a mild form of cracking, or reforming. The octane rating of the petroleum can be further improved if the refining is done in an atmosphere of hydrogen. As can be seen, crude oil contains a wide range of compounds. Many more are made when it is refined. These compounds are the starting materials for the petrochemical industry. The petrochemical industry produces a wide range of plastics, fabrics, drugs, explosives, and other products.

The several processes, such as distilling, vacuum distilling, and cracking, can be varied. This depends on the demand for different products.

Production of petroleum New reservoirs of petroleum are being tapped. Some of the most productive are those in Alaska and in the North Sea between Britain and mainland Europe.

Oil can be taken from oil shale. It can also be taken from tar sands. Because oil can be made from coal and hydrogen, coal deposits remain the most valuable source for future oil supplies. Coal is itself a source of energy because it burns. It does not, however, provide the many petrochemicals that are by-products of petroleum. When scientists predict that the world's petroleum supply will be used up by the end of the 20th century, they are not just saying that new sources of energy must be found. They are also saying that our way of life will be changed.   J.J.A./J.M.

PETROLOGY (pə träl′ ə jē) Petrology is the study of rocks. This branch of geology deals with the formation, chemical composition, and structure of rocks. Petrologists also study the effect of erosion on rocks, as well as other ways by which rocks change. (*See* METAMORPHIC ROCK.) Petrography deals with the classification and description of rocks. *See also* EROSION; IGNEOUS ROCK; SEDIMENTARY ROCK.   J.M.C./W.R.S.

PEWEE (pē′ wē) The pewee is a small bird that belongs to the family Tyrannidae. It is mostly olive-brown with white bars on its wings. The pewee grows to 12 cm [5 in] long. There are two species of pewees that are common in North America. The eastern wood pewee lives in most areas east of the Missouri River. The western wood pewee lives in most areas west of the Missouri. Pewees live in wooded places and eat insects.

S.R.G./L.L.S.

PEWTER (pyüt′ ər) Pewter is an alloy consisting chiefly of tin, with small amounts of antimony and copper. Pewter has a color similar to silver and a finish that may vary from dull to glossy.

Most pewter contains at least 90 percent tin, which is a very soft metal. Antimony and copper are added to give pewter hardness and strength. At one time, much pewter contained lead. But lead could dissolve in some foods and beverages in pewter ware, forming toxic substances. Lead also caused tarnishing. As a result, britannia metal came into use in Britain during the 1700s. Britannia metal consisted of tin, antimony, and copper—the alloy did not tarnish.

Today, britannia metal and pewter are nearly identical. Pewter articles, such as candlesticks, mugs, and pitchers, may be made of either alloy.   J.J.A./A.D.

Shown below is an eastern wood pewee.

PH Chemists use a pH number to show the strength of an acid or base. The number is generally on a scale from 0 to 14. A pH under 7 indicates that the solution is an acid. A pH more than 7 indicates that the solution is a base. Strong acids have lower pHs than weak acids. Strong bases have higher pHs than weak bases. A neutral solution is neither an acid or a base. It has a pH of 7.

A pH number indicates the concentration (number per liter) of hydrogen ions in a solution. The pH of a solution is defined as the negative logarithm, to the base 10, of its hydrogen concentration. This concentration is expressed in moles of hydrogen ions per liter of solution. For example, a solution with a pH of 10 contains 10^{-10} of a mole of hydrogen ions per liter. (*See* MOLE (UNIT).) An electronic pH meter or special dyes called acid-base indicators are used to measure pH. *See also* ACID; BASE.   J.J.A./A.D.

PHALANGES (fə lan′ jēz) Phalanges are the small bones in the fingers, thumbs, and toes of the human body. Each finger contains three phalanges, and each thumb has two. There are 14 phalanges in the toes of a foot—three in each toe except the big toe, which has two.   W.R.P./J.J.F.

PHARMACOLOGY (far′ mə käl′ ə jē) Pharmacology is the branch of science and medicine that studies the effects of drugs on living organisms. (*See* DRUG.) Pharmacology combines biology and chemistry in finding out how drugs change the workings of tissues and organs.

Pharmacology includes many other specialized areas of study. Chemotherapy uses specific drugs to treat disease. Psychopharmacology studies drugs that affect behavior. Pharmacogenetics studies the effects of drugs on hereditary factors. Toxicology studies poisonous and potentially poisonous drugs. Pharmacy involves preparing and giving out drugs.   A.J.C./J.J.F.

Pharmaceutical samples are being tested in a laboratory.

PHASE (fāz′) Phase has several different meanings in science. In physics, phase refers to wave motions such as light and sound. If two waves are vibrating together exactly, they are said to be in phase. They can then make each other stronger. If they are completely out of phase, they can cancel each other out. (*See* BEAT.)

In chemistry, a mixture of water and ice is called a two-phase system. This is because there is a definite boundary between the water and the ice. Salt dissolved in water is a one-phase system. There is no boundary between the salt and the water.

In astronomy, the moon and other planets go through phases. As the moon goes round the earth, different parts of the moon are lit up by the sun. The different appearances of the moon are called phases. In the same way, planets have different phases as they travel round the sun.   M.E./R.W.L.

PHEASANT (fez′ ənt) The pheasant is a large bird of the Phasianidae family. The male is colorful, and the female is brown. There are many species of pheasants in Asia, but one species, the ring-necked pheasant, has brought to the United States and Canada. It is a popular game bird. Although the pheasant lives in many places, it does best in grassy fields. It feeds on grain, seeds, and fruits. The ring-necked pheasant received its name because the male bird has a white ring of feathers around its neck. Pheasants grow to about 70 cm [28 in] long. *See also* BIRD.   S.R.G./L.L.S.

PHENOLS (fē′ nōlz′) Phenols are a group of organic chemical compounds. They contain one or more hydroxyl groups (OH) attached to a benzene ring. They are similar to alcohols. (*See* ALCOHOL.) Alcohols, however, usually have a hydroxyl group attached to a chain of carbon atoms. Like alcohols, phenols combine with organic acids to form compounds called esters. (*See* ESTER.) Phenols can also act as weak acids. They form salts called phenates. In a phenate, the hydrogen atom in the hydroxyl group is replaced by a metal atom.

Phenols are found in coal tar. They are used to make dyes, disinfectants, drugs, and plastics. Phenol is also the name given to the simplest phenol compound. Its formula is C_6H_5OH. It is also known as carbolic acid. Phenol is obtained from coal tar but can also be made artificially. It is a strong antiseptic and is both poisonous and corrosive.

M.E./J.M.

PHEROMONE (fer′ ə mōn′) Pheromones are special chemicals produced by animals that make other animals of the same kind behave in a particular way. They are one of the ways in which animals can communicate with one another. When a tomcat marks out his territory by spraying posts with very strong-smelling urine he is using a pheromone. It tells other tomcats to keep away from his territory. This is an obvious example; the odor is very powerful. But scientists have discovered other pheromones that are not obvious to humans. Moths produce pheromones that attract their mates. Social insects, such as ants and honeybees, use pheromones in various ways. Ants use them to mark food trails and to signal when to attack and when to flee. Worker bees mark the nest of their colony with pheromones to help bees returning from food gathering to distinguish their nest from others. When it is time to mate, the queen bees secrete a pheromone that attracts the drones.

When human beings enter adolescence, their perspiration takes on an odor. The production of the pheromones responsible for this odor is one of the changes in the chemistry of the body that take place with sexual maturity. *See also* HORMONE.   C.M./C.R.N.

PHLEBITIS (fli bīt′ əs) Phlebitis is an inflammation of the wall of a vein. It usually occurs when part of the lining of a vein becomes damaged or diseased. The wall of the vein swells and becomes painful. From the outside, the vein looks enlarged and reddened. Phlebitis is dangerous because blood tends to clot wherever the smooth wall of a blood vessel is damaged and roughened. This clot (or thrombus) may increase in size and may eventually block the vein. A clot that has broken off and is being carried in the bloodstream is called an embolus. If an embolus carries bacteria with it, it will spread the infection to other parts of the body. If the embolus settles in the heart or lungs, it may be fatal.

Phlebitis may be treated with drugs to prevent the blood from clotting. If there is an infection, antibiotics may be used. In severe cases, a surgeon may have to remove a length of badly damaged vein. *See also* CIRCULATORY SYSTEM; VEIN.   D.M.H.W./J.J.F.

PHLOEM (flō′ em′) Phloem is the food-carrying tissue found in the leaves, stems, and roots of vascular plants. (*See* VASCULAR PLANT.) It takes sugar and other foods produced by photosynthesis from the leaves to all other parts of the plant. (*See* PHOTOSYNTHESIS.)

The phloem of angiosperms is made up of tube-shaped cells arranged end to end. There are small holes in the ends of the cells so that there is a continuous tube for food transport. Each cell is called a sieve tube. It is living, has cytoplasm, but has no nucleus. Next to each sieve tube is a nucleus-containing companion cell. The companion cell apparently controls the working of the sieve tube cell. There are usually fibers extending through the phloem for more strength. The phloem of dicotyledons is arranged in an orderly pattern. In woody plants, it is part of the inner bark. The phloem of monocotyledons is arranged in random bundles with the xylem throughout the stem. (*See* XYLEM.)

The phloem of gymnosperms and ferns is made of irregularly shaped cells with many perforated areas (areas with holes) on all surfaces. These perforated areas are called sieve plates. These plants have no companion cells. See also ANGIOSPERM; DICOTYLEDON; GYMNOSPERM; MONOCOTYLEDON.   A.J.C./M.H.S.

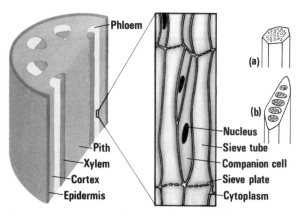

Phloem tissue contains two kinds of living cells—sieve tubes and companion cells. Sieve tubes have no nuclei and conduct fluids up and down the plant. Companion cells have nuclei, which help maintain the sieve tubes. Fluids pass from one sieve tube to another through sieve plates—cell walls perforated by holes. The two kinds of sieve plates are (a) simple and (b) compound.

PHLOX (fläks′) Phlox is a genus with about 65 species, all but one of which are native to North America. They belong to the family Polemoniaceae.

Most phlox are perennials. Their simple leaves occur in opposite pairs close to the ground, but often become alternate higher up. (*See* LEAF.) Their brilliant flowers grow in clusters, each flower having five petals.

The summer phlox (*Phlox paniculata*) grows to heights of 150 cm [60 in]. Summer phlox is a popular garden plant in eastern North America. Blue phlox (*Phlox divaricata*) is noted for its blue and white flowers that bloom each spring.   J.M.C./M.H.S.

Phlox (above) is a popular garden flower.

PHOEBE (fē′ be) The phoebe is a small bird that belongs to the flycatcher family Tyrannidae. It has a large head, slender bill, and a long tail which it twitches frequently. There are three species of phoebe in North America: the black phoebe in the southwest, Say's

Marine animals that live in deep, inky-dark waters, such as this squid, are often phosphorescent.

phoebe in the west, and the eastern phoebe in the east. The phoebes eat insects and nest in rock crevices, under bridges, and beneath overhanging porches. *See also* BIRD.

S.R.G./L.L.S.

PHOSPHATE (fäs′ fāt′) Phosphates are salts of any of the phosphoric acids. They are found in many different minerals. The most important phosphate is calcium phosphate. Calcium phosphate is found in bones and is used as a fertilizer. If calcium phosphate is treated with sulfuric acid, calcium hydrogen phosphate is formed. Calcium hydrogen phosphate is used in fertilizers called superphosphates. It dissolves in water and can be more easily absorbed by plants than calcium phosphate. This makes it a better fertilizer.

M.E./A.D.

PHOSPHORESCENCE (fäs′ fə res′ əns) Phosphorescence is a glowing light that is released slowly from a substance. Atoms consist of a central core, or nucleus, surrounded by electrons. The electrons circle the nucleus in orbits. Electrons in a higher orbit have more energy than electrons in a lower orbit. (*See* ATOM.)

When light shines on certain materials, their electrons absorb the light. The energy of the light causes the electrons to jump into higher orbits. They then give out the light and return to their original orbits. This is called luminescence. (*See* LUMINESCENCE.) If the light is given out immediately, the effect is called fluorescence. (*See* FLUORESCENCE.) If the light energy is stored and released over a period of time, it is called phosphorescence. Phosphorescent materials glow in the dark. Certain luminous paints are made of phosphorescent substances. Some animals found in the sea are phosphorescent. This is called bioluminescence. (*See* BIOLUMINESCENCE.)

M.E./S.S.B.

PHOSPHORIC ACID (fäs fòr' ik as' əd) Many acids are made by dissolving an oxide in water. Phosphorus forms an oxide called phosphorus pentoxide (P_4O_{10}). It dissolves in water to form acids called phosphoric acids. The most important of these acids are orthophosphoric acid (H_3PO_4), pyrophosphoric acid ($H_4P_2O_7$), and metaphosphoric acid (HPO_3). Orthophosphoric acid is made in industry by treating calcium phosphate with sulfuric acid. Calcium phosphate is a salt of phosphoric acid. When it is heated to 220°C [428°F], it changes into pyrophosphoric acid. On further heating to 320°C [608°F], metaphosphoric acid is formed. Orthophosphoric acid is used in refining sugar and in manufacturing glass.   M.E./A.D.

PHOSPHORUS (fàs' fə rəs) Phosphorus (P) is a solid nonmetallic element. Its atomic number is 15 and its atomic weight is 30.9738. It melts at 44.1°C [111.4°F] and boils at 280°C [536°F].

Phosphorus occurs in several different forms. These different forms are called allotropes. (*See* ALLOTROPE.) The best-known form is called yellow or white phosphorus because of its color. The melting and boiling points given above are those of white phosphorus. It is a poisonous waxy solid with a relative density of 1.8. It is very reactive and may catch fire in air. Therefore it is stored under water. If white phosphorus is heated to 250°C [480°F] or is exposed to sunlight, it changes into another allotrope called red phosphorus. Red phosphorus is not so reactive and does not catch fire in air. Red phosphorus is not poisonous and is slightly heavier than white phosphorus. Its relative density is 2.2.

Phosphorus was discovered in 1669 by Hennig Brand, a German alchemist. It is used in making matches and smoke bombs. The most important compounds of phosphorus are salts called phosphates. Phosphates are salts of acids called phosphoric acids. Phosphates are very important fertilizers. Phosphorus is essential to life; bones are mainly made of calcium phosphate.   M.E./J.R.W.

PHOTOELECTRIC EFFECT (fōt' ō i lek' trik i fekt') When light strikes the surface of certain substances, especially metals, small particles called electrons are given off, or deflected. This process is called photoemission. It is an example of the photoelectric effect. Any effect in which light produces electrical effects is called a photoelectric effect. Very often though, the term photoelectric effect means photoemission. X rays and ultraviolet light can also cause photoemission in many substances.

Photoemission was first explained by the physicist Albert Einstein. (*See* EINSTEIN, ALBERT.) Light and other radiation is made up of small packets of energy called photons. The frequency of light is the number of times that it vibrates in a second. The higher the frequency, the more energy the photons have. Ultraviolet light has a higher frequency than visible light. Therefore photons of ultraviolet light have more energy than photons of visible light. If a photon hits an atom, it may be absorbed by an electron. If the photon has enough energy, then the electron is ejected from the metal surface.

There are other photoelectric effects. A very similar effect to photoemission is photoionization. Photoionization occurs in certain gases. If radiation passes through the gas, the photons may collide with the molecules in the gas. These collisions can knock the electrons out of the molecules. The gas becomes ionized. (*See* IONS AND IONIZATION.) That is why the effect is called photoionization.

Another photoelectric effect occurs when radiation hits a semiconductor. Semiconductors contain free, negatively charged electrons and positively charged holes. (*See* SEMICONDUCTOR.) A free electron is an electron that is not bound to any atom. It can move freely throughout the substance. These electrons and holes can conduct electricity. When radiation falls on certain semiconductors, the number of electrons and holes increases. This changes the current through the semiconductor. This is called photoconductivity.

The photovoltaic effect is similar to photoconductivity. In this effect, radiation falls on two semiconductors, or on a metal and a semiconductor sandwiched together. A potential difference develops across the boundary between the two substances. The electrons cannot flow across the boundary. If the two substances are connected in a circuit, then the electrons can leave one of the substances and flow through the circuit.

Photoelectric devices Photoelectric effects are used in many different devices. The photovoltaic effect is used in exposure meters for photography. (*See* EXPOSURE METER.) Light falling on the meter causes a current to flow around a circuit. The size of the current depends on the amount of light. This allows the amount of light to be measured.

In recent years, photoconductors have

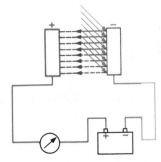

Photoelectric effect is illustrated. When a metal is exposed to light of a certain wavelength, it emits electrons (negatively-charged particles). Each metal is sensitive to light of a different wavelength. If two metal plates, separated by an air gap, are connected to a battery through a galvanometer (an instrument for measuring current flow), no current will flow because of the gap between the plates. If the negatively-charged plate is exposed to light of the appropriate wavelength for that metal, electrons will leave the surface, and will be attracted to the positively charged plate. This flow of electrons (electric current) will be indicated by the galvanometer, and will continue while the negative plate remains exposed to the light source.

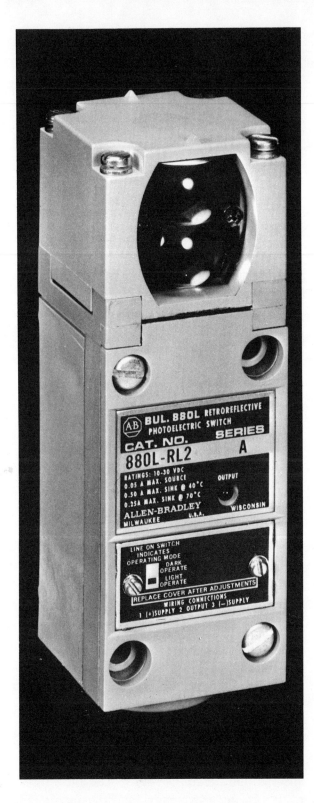

Shown above is the switch of a photoelectric cell. A beam of light is focussed on the lens of the switch. If the beam is broken, the switch can set off an alarm, open a door, etc.

largely replaced photoemitters. They are more efficient and can detect light with lower frequencies. They are used in television cameras, burglar alarms, and many other devices. M.E./S.S.B.

PHOTOGRAPHY

An overexposed photograph is too light in color.

Photography (fə täg′ rə fē) is the process of taking pictures with a camera. The word photography means "drawing with light." A camera picture is a picture drawn with rays of light.

Photography enriches our lives in many ways. Illustrations in newspapers, magazines, and books are usually made from photographs. Photography is an important tool in advertising, business, and industry. It even helps people explore the earth, the oceans, and outer space. Some photographs have lasting artistic value, like some paintings.

Photography is one of the most popular hobbies in the world. For example, almost half of the families in the United States own a camera. Many people join camera clubs all over the world to meet with other camera enthusiasts. Sometimes they display their photographs at exhibitions in art galleries and museums.

An underexposed photograph is too dark in color.

Motion pictures make up a special branch of photography. Many of the principles used in still photography are used in making motion pictures. (*See* MOTION PICTURE.)

Taking photographs can be easy today. Most modern cameras do much of the work automatically. All you do is load the camera with film, point it at what you want to photograph, and press the shutter button. (*See* CAMERA.)

Exposing the film. Light is the key to photography. To produce a perfect picture, every film must be exposed to a certain amount of

In this photograph, the film has been correctly exposed. Correct exposure of the film is essential to capture all the details in the subject.

light. Too much light results in overexposure, and the photograph is foggy. Too little light results in underexposure, and the picture is dark.

Films have different speeds, or sensitivity to light. Some films are extremely sensitive, or fast. Others are less sensitive, or slow. Fast

These photos of a water splash were taken at a shutter speed of 1/5000 second. By means of high speed photography, events can be recorded which happen too quickly for us to see them.

films require relatively brief exposures. Slow films require relatively long exposures. In the United States, film speed is expressed numerically based upon standards set by the American Standards Association (ASA). A film that rates ASA 50 is a slow film. One that rates about ASA 400 is a fast film.

The exposure of film can be varied in two major ways. First, the exposure time, during which the shutter is open, can be altered. Second, for any given exposure time, the amount of light entering the camera can be increased or decreased. This is done by changing the size of the lens opening, or aperture, with a diaphragm which blocks off part of the lens. Several different combinations of aperture settings and shutter speeds make it possible to get the proper settings for all conditions of light. The selection depends upon the particular type of subject being photographed, the effect required, and the camera involved.

A fast speed of 1/500th of a second would be required to take a non-blurred photograph of a galloping horse. A large aperture of around f/4 could be required to give the correct exposure. But this would show only the horse in focus. The background would be out of focus because the depth of field is shallow at large aperture settings. Depth of field is the range within which objects are clear and sharply defined. Objects beyond or nearer this range are blurred. To get the background in focus, the aperture must be reduced to approximately f/16. But, to get the same exposure, we would have to increase the exposure time to 1/30th of a second. At this shutter speed, the horse would appear blurred on the film.

A device called an exposure meter, or light meter, can be used to measure the brightness of the scene being photographed. This enables a suitable aperture to be chosen. Most exposure meters work on a photoelectric principle. (*See* PHOTOELECTRIC EFFECT.) Many cameras have built-in meters. In dim lighting conditions, such as the interior of a church, an exposure of several seconds may be necessary. Most cameras have a setting that allows the shutter to be held open as long as necessary. Electronic flash units are usually used to illuminate the scene or subject in dim light conditions. The flash is synchronized with the opening of the shutter. Flash units, which are built into the camera or attached to it, can also be used in complete darkness.

Developing and printing. Black-and-white film has a light-sensitive coating of tiny grains of silver bromide crystals. When these grains are exposed to light, they tend to break down and deposit dark grains of silver. However, this process is only completed through the chemical actions of a solution of devel-

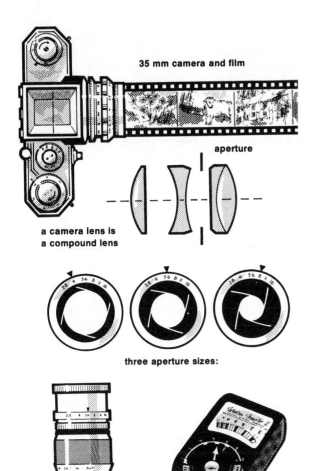

35 mm camera and film

aperture

**a camera lens is
a compound lens**

three aperture sizes:

telephoto lens

exposure meter

Photographic equipment is shown above. The lens of a camera is made up of a combination of lenses. The amount of light that reaches the film is regulated by the size of the aperture. An exposure meter and a telephoto lens (for cameras with detachable lenses) are useful accessories.

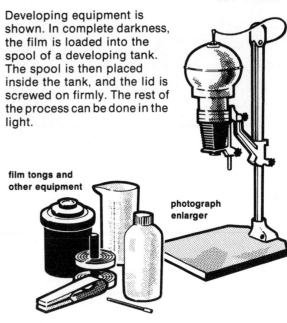

Developing equipment is shown. In complete darkness, the film is loaded into the spool of a developing tank. The spool is then placed inside the tank, and the lid is screwed on firmly. The rest of the process can be done in the light.

**film tongs and
other equipment**

**photograph
enlarger**

oper. During development, parts of the film that were most exposed to light deposit the most silver and become dark. Meanwhile, unexposed places remain unchanged. In a later stage, called fixing, the unchanged grains are dissolved away, leaving clear film. After fixing, the film is washed and dried. All gradations between dark and bright occur according to the pattern of light in the scene photo-

Two examples of multiple exposure photography are shown, facing left. A fast-speed setting is required to take a photo of a moving object.

graphed. However, what was light in the scene becomes dark in the developed film, and vice-versa. Thus, we call the developed film the negative.

Printing is the process of reversing the dark and light tones of the negative into light and dark tones on the paper. The picture obtained is called a positive. The simplest form of printing is contact printing, in which the negative is in contact with the paper. The printing paper is coated with a light-sensitive emulsion, just as the film is. And, after a brief exposure to a bright light, it is exposed, developed, fixed, washed, and dried just like film.

Most photographic printing is done by enlarging and not by contact printing. This is because actual-size prints from most film would be too small for general use. In enlarging, a bright, magnified image of the negative is projected onto the printing paper. Development is then finished the usual way.

Color photography. Color photography is more complicated than black-and-white. Light that looks white to our eyes is really a mixture of all colors of the rainbow. Any color can be reproduced by blending only

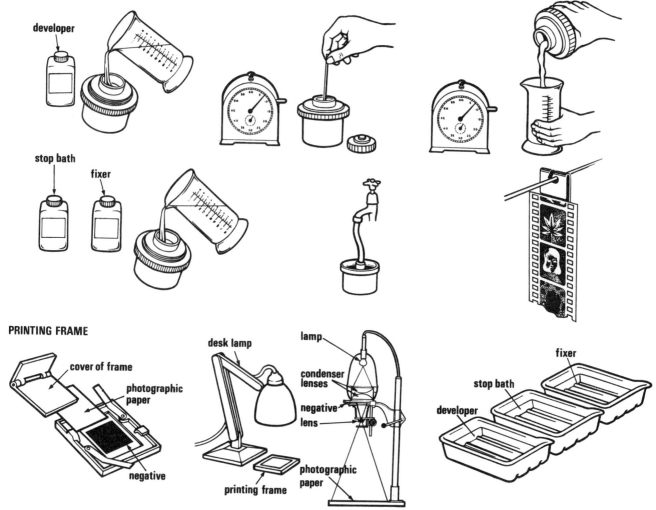

PRINTING FRAME

The developing process is illustrated. First, developer is made up according to the product's instructions and it is poured into the developing tank. Product instructions also give recommended developing times and temperatures. When development is complete, the developer is replaced with a "stop" solution, which prevents overdevelopment. Then the film is fixed with "hypo" solution (sodium hyposulphite), washed with tap water, and hung up to dry. Positive pictures can be made by using a printing frame, in which the negative makes contact with the photographic paper, and a light is shone through the negative onto the paper. If larger prints are needed, an enlarger can be used. The positive print is developed and fixed in dishes with different liquids in them.

three basic colors such as blue, green, and red. These colors are called primary colors of light. In color photography, blue light, red light, and green light are blended in certain proportions to produce any color. (*See* COLOR.)

There are two types of color film: (1) negative and (2) reversal. Negative film produces color negatives from which color prints are made. Reversal film produces color transparencies (slides). A slide is usually viewed in a lighted slide viewer, or through a projector that shines the colored picture onto a screen.

Negative and reversal films are made in almost the same way. Each consists of three layers of emulsion on a sheet of plastic. These emulsions are similar to the emulsions on black-and-white film, but each emulsion is sensitive only to one of three primary colors. The first emulsion is affected only by blue light, the second only by green light, and the third only by red light.

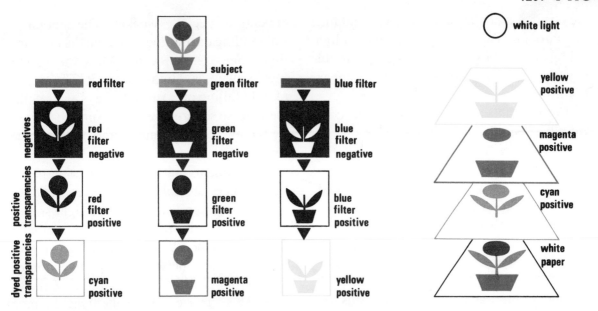

The process of subtractive color photography is illustrated. Color photographs can be made by shining light from the subject through three colored filters (red, green, and blue), and making black and white negatives. Only certain parts of the subject will appear on the negatives. For example, the blue filter will cut out all except the blue light from the object, and the blue parts will appear black (exposed) on the negative. From the negatives, black and white positives are made, which are then dyed with cyan, magenta, and yellow dyes. If the dyed positives are combined, white light shone through them will produce a color image of the original shape.

In this time exposure of a busy street at night, the shutter was open long enough for the lights of the moving cars to produce red and white streaks on the film. The exposure time is the amount of time the shutter on the camera is left open. The amount of light can be increased or decreased.

When color film is exposed, light passes through the first emulsion and records an image of the blue areas of the scene. A special yellow filter layer prevents unused blue light from reaching the other two primary color layers. Then the light passes through the second emulsion layer, which records only the green areas of the scene. Finally, the light passes through the third emulsion layer, which records the red areas. The three images are not colored on the film. They are dyed during the developing process.

Color film is developed in a special developer. It changes the exposed silver salts on the emulsions to metallic silver. A silver image forms in each emulsion layer. The developing solution then causes colored dyes to form in each layer by reacting with substances called couplers. A yellow dye forms in the first layer. A magenta (bluish red) dye forms in the second layer, and a cyan (bluish green) dye forms in the third layer. These three colors are complementary, or direct opposites, to the three primary colors. Complementary colors reproduce the original colors when light is passed through the film.

Each dye acts as a filter to a primary color. The yellow dye absorbs blue light and lets red and green light pass through. The magenta dye absorbs green light and lets red and blue pass through. The cyan dye absorbs red light and lets blue and green pass through. In this way, the original colors of the subject appear in a print.

Color reversal film that produces color slides has a similar developing process. However, there is one extra step. The film is re-exposed after the first development so that remaining silver salts can be developed. During the second development, colored dyes form around the silver images of the subject. The silver is then bleached out, leaving transparent film in those areas. In the developed film, a yellow dye surrounds the image made by blue light, magenta dye surrounds the green light image, and cyan dye surrounds the red light image. When the film is projected, each dye holds back light of the complementary color, and the original colors of the subject appear on the screen. *See also* POLAROID CAMERA. W.R.P./R.W.L.

PHOTOMETRY (fō täm′ ə trē) Photometry is concerned with the measurement of light. The amount of light given out by a light source is called the luminous flux. It is measured in units called lumens. (*See* LUMEN.) Light sources are often compared to a standard light source. This standard source is called a standard candle or a candela. A candela gives out 4π lumens.

As we move away from a light source, it appears to become weaker. The amount of light falling on a surface is called the illumination. (*See* ILLUMINATION.) As the surface moves away, less light falls on it. The amount of light falling on a surface obeys a law called the inverse square law. If the surface is twice as far away, the illumination falls to one-fourth. (*See* INVERSE SQUARE LAW.)

Instruments that measure the brightness of light sources are called photometers. Photometers most often use a standard light source. The light source that is to be measured is compared to the standard source. The photometer is placed between these two sources. Light from each source falls onto a dull surface. This surface scatters the light. Some of the light from each source passes through prisms. The prisms deflect the light into an eyepiece. The distance from the photometer to the light sources is then adjusted. At a certain distance, the two sources look equally bright in the eyepiece. By using the inverse square law, scientists can calculate the brightness of the unknown source.

A different method is used for measuring the brightness of daylight. A device called a barrier layer cell is used. This is made of a metal and a piece of selenium. Selenium is a nonmetallic element. When light falls on the cell, a voltage develops in it. This causes a current to flow in a circuit that contains an ammeter or volt-meter. The size of the current depends on the brightness of the daylight. In

Flame photometers are used to analyze substances. The substance is dissolved in liquid, which is then sucked up and sprayed through distributing filters to a gas flame. The wavelengths of the light from the flame are changed by the substance. The light then passes through optical filters. Specific wavelengths reach a detector. The specific wavelengths are characteristic of the substance, so that it can be identified and its quantity measured.

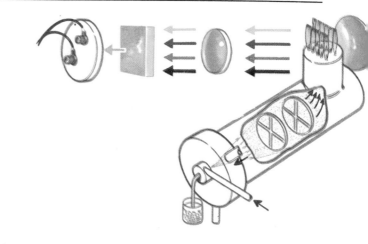

this way, the brightness of the light can be measured. This system is used in exposure meters for cameras. (*See* EXPOSURE METER.)

M.E./S.S.B.

PHOTON (fō′ tän′) In many ways, light behaves like a wave. For example, light exhibits interference and diffraction. These are wave effects. However, the wave theory of light cannot explain certain phenomena. These can only be explained by regarding light as a stream of particles. These particles are called photons. They were first suggested to exist by Albert Einstein in 1905. Light is a form of electromagnetic radiation. All electromagnetic radiation, such as radio waves and ultraviolet rays, consist of photons. *See also* LIGHT; PHOTOELECTRIC EFFECT.

M.E./R.W.L.

PHOTOPERIODISM (fōt′ ō pir′ ē əd iz′ əm) Photoperiodism is the response of a living organism to the length of day or night, or both. The photoperiod, or critical day length, is the number of hours of light needed to cause this response. Some examples of photoperiodism are the migration of birds and the breeding of many animals. (*See* BIOLOGICAL RHYTHM.)

Photoperiodism most commonly refers to the appearance of flowers on a flowering plant. Short-day plants, such as poinsettias and strawberries, flower when the day is shorter than a certain number of hours. Most short-day plants bloom in the early spring or late fall. Long-day plants, such as spinach and lettuce, flower when the day is longer than a certain number of hours. Most long-day plants bloom in the summer. Neutral-day plants are not affected by the length of the day.

Photoperiodism in plants is controlled by a light-sensitive, bluish pigment called phytochrome. (*See* PIGMENT.) Florists often use their knowledge of photoperiodism to produce flowers year-round, particularly during holiday seasons when flowers are most in demand. They do this by artificially controlling the lengths of the "days" and "nights" in greenhouses where the flowers are grown.

A.J.C./M.H.S.

PHOTOSYNTHESIS (fōt′ ō sin′ thə səs) Photosynthesis is the process by which green plants make food. It is the only known naturally occurring process that changes inorganic substances (carbon dioxide and water) into an organic substance (food). In addition, oxygen is made as an end-product and released into the air. Photosynthesis is a complex series of chemical reactions that uses energy from sunlight to make food and oxygen from carbon dioxide and water—all in the presence of chlorophyll.

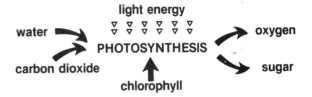

Chlorophyll is a green pigment found in tiny structures called chloroplasts. (*See* CHLOROPHYLL.) Without chlorophyll, photosynthesis cannot take place. In higher plants, most of the chloroplasts are found in the cells of the leaves. (*See* LEAF.) Water is absorbed by the roots and taken to the leaves. (*See* ROOT.) Carbon dioxide enters the leaves through tiny openings called stomata. (*See* STOMA.)

The food made by photosynthesis is glucose, a sugar. The glucose may be taken throughout the plant and used by the cells and tissues as a source of chemical energy. Some of the glucose is combined with nitrogen to form amino acids, proteins, or nucleic acids. Nitrogen is usually dissolved in water absorbed by the roots. Some of the glucose is changed to cellulose and used to build up plant tissues. (*See* CELLULOSE.) Some of the glucose is also changed to starch and stored in the leaves, stem, or roots.

All food comes either directly or indirectly from photosynthesis. Many animals eat plants for food. Other animals—including human beings—eat plants and plant-eating animals. Thus, photosynthetic plants are a vital part of the food chain. (*See* FOOD CHAIN.)

Most plants and animals get the energy they need through respiration. (*See* RESPIRATION.) In respiration, food and oxygen are used to make energy, carbon dioxide, and water. It can be seen, then, that respiration and photosynthesis are opposite reactions, and occur in a continuous cycle. The end-products of one reaction are the raw materials needed for the other.

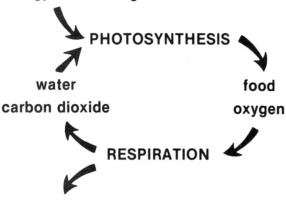

energy from sunlight

PHOTOSYNTHESIS

water   **food**

carbon dioxide   **oxygen**

RESPIRATION

energy for cellular activity

It is believed that photosynthetic plants produced all the oxygen in the atmosphere as the earth was developing. (*See* EARTH.) Since that time, the amount of oxygen in the air (about 21%) and the amount of carbon dioxide in the air (about 0.04%) have remained fairly constant as a result of photosynthesis. (See AIR.)

Of all the photosynthesis that takes place, more than 75% takes place in the oceans, in tiny plants called phytoplankton. (*See* PLANKTON.) Scientists are constantly seeking ways to use these marine plants as a food source for human beings. Scientists are also trying to find ways of increasing the amount of photosynthesis that takes place in land plants in hopes of increasing the world food supply. They have found that factors such as temperature, light intensity, water supply, and carbon dioxide supply all affect the rate of photosynthesis up to a point. The rate, however, is limited by factors such as enzymes which affect rates of many of the chemical reactions in photosynthesis. *See also* ATP; CARBON CYCLE; WATER CYCLE.

A.J.C./M.H.S.

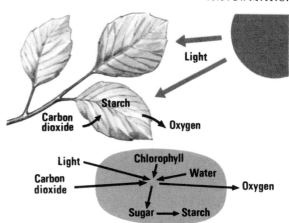

Photosynthesis takes place during daylight. Carbon dioxide is taken into the leaf and converted to starch, and oxygen is released into the air.

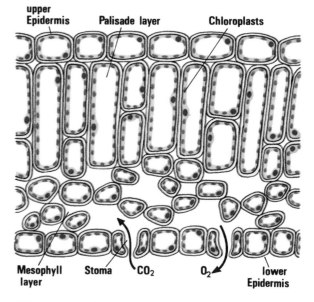

This cross section of a leaf shows carbon dioxide entering through the stomata (bottom). Photosynthesis takes place in the chloroplasts (top). The combination of light, carbon dioxide, water, and chlorophyll produces sugar and oxygen. The oxygen passes out through the stomata, and the sugar is stored as starch.

PHYLUM (fī' ləm) A phylum, in the classification of living organisms, is a subdivision of a kingdom. It is made up of a group of related classes. *See also* CLASS; CLASSIFICATION OF LIVING ORGANISMS; KINGDOM. A.J.C./C.R.N.

PHYSICAL CHANGE (fiz' i kəl chānj') A physical change is any change that occurs to a substance without affecting its chemical composition. For example, a physical change occurs when ice melts to form water. Both ice and water have the same chemical composition: H_2O. Therefore, there is no chemical change. The change is physical. If the ice had broken down into hydrogen and oxygen, then this would be a chemical change.

In many solids, the atoms or molecules are arranged in a regular pattern. This pattern is called a crystal lattice. The lattice always has a definite shape. Under very high pressures, the shape of the lattice can be altered. This is another example of a physical change. Many properties of solids depend on their lattice shape. Changing the lattice shape can sometimes change the physical properties of a solid. For example, very high pressures can change a solid that conducts electricity into one that does not. M.E./A.D.

PHYSICAL CHEMISTRY (fiz' i kəl kem' ə strē) Physical chemistry is the study of the physical properties of chemical compounds and reactions. It studies the effect of physical factors such as heat, light and electricity. Physical chemists also measure physical properties of substances such as melting and boiling points and molecular weights. Another important branch of physical chemistry is the study of molecular structure. This includes the arrangement of the atoms in a molecule and different kinds of bonding. *See also* CHEMISTRY. M.E./J.T.

PHYSICS (fiz' iks) Physics is the study of the properties of matter and energy. Physicists try to understand the universe by searching for the basic laws of nature. They do this by performing experiments. Then they propose a law that explains the results of these experiments. The proposed law can be used to predict other effects. These effects must also be tested by experiment. If they fit the proposed law, then the law becomes established. Most laws have been shown to be at least slightly inaccurate. A new law is then proposed to explain the new results. For example, Sir Isaac Newton's theory of mechanics was accepted for more than 200 years, until the beginning of this century. However, experiments on objects moving at almost the speed of light could not be explained by Newton's theory. A new theory, the theory of relativity, was devised by Albert Einstein to explain these new results. (*See* RELATIVITY.)

Most physical laws are stated mathematically. Mathematics is a very important and powerful tool for a physicist. Many experiments in physics involve measurements. The measurements give numbers that can be treated mathematically.

Nowadays it is difficult to divide physics into separate branches. This is because more and more overlapping areas of the different branches are being discovered. However, for convenience, physics is still divided into mechanics, heat, light, sound, electricity and magnetism, and solid state physics. There are also branches that cover atomic, nuclear, and particle physics.

Mechanics is the study of material bodies and the forces that act on them. It is divided into two main branches: statics and dynamics. Statics is the study of forces acting on a body at rest, such as the forces acting on a bridge. Dynamics is the study of forces that cause bodies to move, such as the forces acting on a swinging pendulum. (*See* MECHANICS.)

Heat studies are concerned with the effect of temperature on various substances. Heat is a form of energy. It can be changed into different forms of energy such as mechanical or electrical energy. Thermodynamics is the branch of ''heat physics'' that is the study of the transformation of energy. (*See* HEAT; THERMODYNAMICS.)

The study of light is called optics. It investigates the nature and properties of light. An important part of optics is the study of optical instruments such as telescopes and microscopes. (*See* OPTICS.)

Sound is studied in a branch of physics called acoustics. Acoustics is the study of properties of sound such as the ways in which sound is transmitted through air and other materials, and how sound is produced. An important part of acoustics is the design of acoustical buildings such as concert halls, and acoustical equipment. (*See* ACOUSTICS.)

Electricity and magnetism were once considered to be two separate subjects. During the 1800s, however, several connections were discovered between them. Electricity and magnetism are now studied as a single subject. The study of the connections between electricity and magnetism is called electromagnetism. (*See* ELECTRICITY; MAGNETISM.)

Solid state physics is a recent branch of physics. It explains the properties of a solid in terms of its atoms. One of the results of solid state physics has been the invention of the transistor. Transistors are now used in many different electronic devices. (*See* SOLID STATE PHYSICS.)

Atomic, nuclear, and particle physics are also recent branches of physics. Atomic and nuclear physics include the study of the atom and the nucleus. Particle physics is the study of the particles that make up the nucleus and other subatomic particles. (*See* PARTICLE PHYSICS.) The mathematics needed for these subjects is very advanced. Many of the properties of atoms, nuclei, and particles are explained by quantum theory. (*See* QUANTUM THEORY.)   M.E./J.T.

PHYSICS, HISTORY OF

Physics (fiz′ iks) is the search for laws that can describe the universe. Physics started with the ancient Greeks. They studied it together with biology, chemistry, and astronomy under the title ''natural philoso-

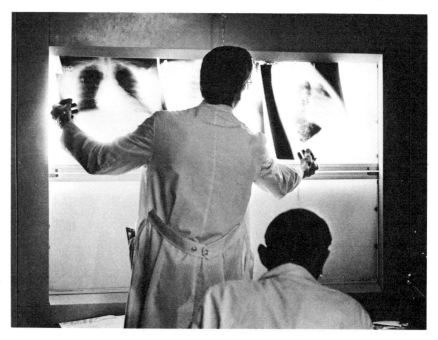

One of the inventions in twentieth-century physics was the X-ray machine In this photograph, technicians are examining X rays of the human chest.

The Archimedes screw (far left) was an early advance in hydrostatics made by Archimedes. The medieval perpetual motion machine (left) was one of many which scientists built only to discover that it did not work.

phy.'' The Greeks based their physical laws on reasoning and common sense. They rarely tested their laws by experiment. Some of their theories were, however, correct. For example, Pythagoras believed that the earth was round. Democritus taught that matter was made up of small particles called atoms. One of the greatest Greek thinkers was Aristotle. Many of his ideas were accepted until the 1500s. One of the few Greeks to perform experiments was Archimedes. He experimented with levers and floating bodies. Some of his laws are still used today.

After the Greeks, little scientific progress was made in Europe until the 1500s. The Arabs translated and preserved many of the Greek writings. They also made their own contributions to science.

During the 1500s, science was once again regarded as a suitable subject for study. The Polish astronomer Nicolaus Copernicus wrote in a book that the earth traveled around the sun. This went against the established opinion which followed Aristotle's view. He believed that the sun traveled around the earth.

Later, the German astronomer Johann Kepler showed that the orbits of the planets were not quite circular. The orbits were ellipses. This also went against established opinion.

Experiments in physics were not really performed until 1600. In that year, the English scientist Sir William Gilbert wrote the first scientific study of magnetism. Gilbert suggested his ideas about magnetism and demonstrated them with experiments. Another great practical physicist of the 1600s was the Italian physicist, Galileo Galilei. Galileo showed that two different weights fall at the same speed if neither is too light. A light weight is noticeably slowed down by air resistance. According to popular legend, he is supposed to have demonstrated this by dropping weights from the Leaning Tower of Pisa. Galileo discovered laws about the motion of bodies. He also improved the recently invented telescope. He used the telescope to show that the earth moves round the sun. His opponents refused to look through his telescope. They stopped him from writing and from continuing his experiments.

One of the most important scientists of the 1600s was Sir Isaac Newton. Newton's theory of gravity explained the orbits of the planets. In mechanics, his laws of motion were accepted for more than 200 years. In optics, Newton was the first to show that white light is a mixture of light of different colors. He thought that light consisted of small particles called corpuscles. At the same time, a Dutch physicist, Christian Huygens, suggested that light was made up of waves.

Many discoveries in electricity and magnetism were made in Michael Faraday's physics laboratory (above) in the 1800s.

Pictured above is Albert Einstein — one of the pioneers of modern physics.

Marconi is pictured in the late 1800s with an early radio.

The laser beam shown below is drilling a hole through a sheet of metal.

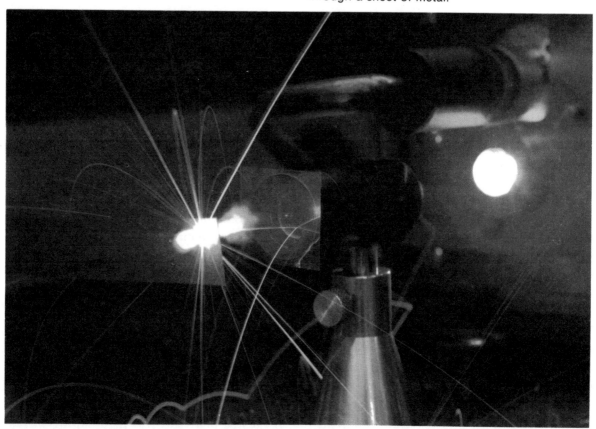

All waves spread out as they move, but light does not. It travels in straight lines. Therefore, Huygens' theory was rejected in favor of Newton's.

During the 1700s, Newton's theories were explored by other scientists. His theories agreed with many of the observations that were made. Only his corpuscular theory of light was proved not to be true. In the early 1800s, the diffraction and interference of light was discovered. The English physicist Thomas Young and the French physicist Augustin Fresnel showed that these effects could be explained by a wave theory.

Also during the 1700s, scientists started to investigate heat and electricity. The study of heat was encouraged by the invention of the steam engine. At first scientists thought that heat was a fluid. When it flowed into a material, the material became hot. The experiments by Count Rumford and James Joule showed that heat was a form of energy. In the early 1800s, John Dalton rediscovered the Greek theory of atoms. It was found that atoms combined to form molecules. Scientists realized that the movement of atoms or molecules caused an object to feel hot. This led to the kinetic theory of gases. This theory helped to explain a number of earlier laws about gases. These discoveries about heat led to the development of thermodynamics. Thermodynamics is the study of ways in which heat energy can be turned into other forms of energy. Thermodynamics helped to explain how a steam engine works.

Electricity and magnetism were known to the ancient Greeks. They tried unsuccessfully to explain these forces. Electricity began to be studied again in the 1700s. The American scientist Benjamin Franklin studied different kinds of electricity—including lightning. During the 1800s, great steps were made in understanding electricity. The most important work was done by an English physicist, Michael Faraday. He discovered that a wire with a current flowing in it acts as a magnet.

His discoveries are the basis of the modern method of generating electricity. (*See* ELECTROMAGNETISM.) In 1873, a Scottish physicist, James Clerk Maxwell, produced a series of equations to describe electricity and magnetism. His equations used the idea of an electromagnetic field. (*See* FIELD.) Using his equations, Maxwell was able to describe a wave. This wave moved through the electromagnetic field. He found that these waves were exactly the same as light. Maxwell had managed to combine optics with electricity and magnetism. In 1886, a German physicist, Heinrich Hertz, discovered another kind of electromagnetic wave, the radio wave.

By the end of the 1800s, physicists thought that all the important laws of physics had been discovered. Then a number of discoveries were made that could not be explained. The French physicists Antoine Becquerel and Marie and Pierre Curie discovered that the atoms of some substances were unstable. They gave off particles and radiation called gamma rays. These atoms are called radioactive atoms. Uranium and radium, for example, are radioactive. A hot body gives off heat in the form of radiation. The theories of heat accepted at that time could not predict the energy of the radiation given off. Several other effects also could not be explained. The German physicist Max Planck suggested that light is given off and absorbed in packets, each of which is called a quantum. This is called the quantum theory.

In 1913, a Danish physicist, Niels Bohr, produced a model of the atom. During the 1920s, two German physicists, Werner Heisenberg and Erwin Schrödinger, improved Bohr's model. With their theory, many effects were explained for the first time. In 1911, the English physicist Lord Rutherford discovered that an atom has a central core called a nucleus. (*See* NUCLEUS, ATOMIC.) During the 1920s and 1930s, the nucleus came to be well understood and radioactivity was explained. It was discovered that the nucleus itself is made of even smaller particles. These particles are called protons and neutrons. Many more subatomic particles have been discovered since then.

Another great theory of this century is the theory of relativity. (*See* RELATIVITY.) It was discovered by the German physicist Albert Einstein. Relativity replaced Newton's theory of mechanics. It also provided a better theory of gravity.

These modern theories have led to many new discoveries and inventions. The nucleus contains a great deal of energy. Once the nucleus was understood, its energy could be tapped. The energy of the nucleus is now used to provide electricity in nuclear power plants. It is also used to build nuclear weapons.

The interest in the atomic nucleus has also been responsible for particle physics, a whole new area of study. Particle physics is concerned with all the elementary particles that make up matter.

The study of elementary particles has enabled great advances to be made in electronics. Radio and radar used to be based on vacuum tubes. Now they use tiny components called transistors. One tiny chip of silicon may contain many transistors. None of these devices could have been invented without a knowledge of elementary particles and quantum theory. (*See* QUANTUM THEORY.)

Astrophysics, too, is a relatively new branch of physics. It deals with the processes that occur in the stars and in space. The evolution of stars and the discoveries of pulsars and quasars have given a new understanding to the ancient science of astronomy. (*See* PULSAR; QUASAR.) M.E./A.I.

PHYSIOLOGY (fiz′ ē äl′ ə jē) Physiology is the study of living things. It is a branch of biology. Physiologists examine the actions of structures and organs in the human body. They learn how these structures and organs work when healthy and when diseased.

Physiology, anatomy, and biochemistry are closely related. Anatomy includes the study of the shape and parts of the body. Biochemistry is the study of the chemicals that make up the body and the chemical changes that go on in living things. For example, the anatomist studies the structure of the stomach muscles and glands. The biochemist studies the chemicals that make up the stomach cells and the chemical changes that occur when the cells pour gastric juices into the stomach. Physiologists are interested in discovering what body activities make the cells secrete gastric juices when food enters the stomach. They also study the churning movements of the stomach.

Physiology is also closely related to medicine, the study of disease. In most diseases, parts of the body are not acting the way they should. Doctors depend upon physiologists to tell them how an organ acts when it is well. Then, they can understand what is happening to the organ when it is diseased.

One of the main benefits of physiology has been diabetes control. Diabetes develops when certain parts of the pancreas do not act the way they should. Many young persons used to die of diabetes each year. In 1922, physiologists completed a long series of experiments with animals. These experiments helped them develop a treatment for diabetes in humans. This treatment has since saved the lives of many thousands of diabetic people. See also ANATOMY; BIOCHEMISTRY; MEDICINE. W.R.P./J.J.F.

PHYSIOTHERAPY (fiz′ ē ō ther′ ə pē) Physiotherapy, also known as physical therapy, is the use of any physical agent and/or exercise to treat a disease or injury. It is part of the branch of medicine called rehabilitation medicine. Doctors who specialize in this branch of medicine are called physiatrists. Treatments prescribed by these doctors are given by people called physical therapists.

Physiotherapy is helpful in treating many

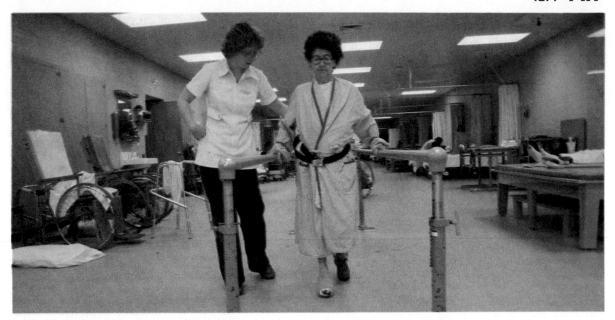

The patient above is exercising in the
physiotherapy section of a hospital.

kinds of disabilities and diseases. It is often
used in treating various kinds of paralysis and
muscle weaknesses such as poliomyletis and
multiple sclerosis. It is also used in treating
heart and lung diseases. Physiotherapy can be
prescribed as treatment for amputations, frac-
tures, and other injuries. With the aid of
physiotherapy, the disabled person may be
able to lead a constructive and creative life.

Many kinds of devices and treatments are
used in physiotherapy. Radiant heat lamps,
electric heating pads, diathermy (electric heat
treatment), hydrotherapy (water treatment),
and special baths are used to apply heat to
diseased or damaged parts of the body. Heat
relieves pain and improves circulation. Cold,
used soon after certain injuries, lessens pain
and swelling. Ultraviolet radiation is used to
attack germs and to help healing. Ultrasound
is used to treat inflammatory conditions of
muscles and joints.

Exercise is an important part of physiotherapy. In fact, many people believe that
it is the only thing physiotherapists con-
cern themselves with. There is, however, a lot
more to their work. They do help patients
exercise and they encourage patients to do

many physical things on their own. Often,
they work with equipment such as pulleys,
weights, parallel bars, stationary bicycles,
and dumbells. Splints, braces, crutches, and
wheel chairs also help disabled patients perform daily activities. Physiotherapists help
people learn to use all of these devices and
develop confidence in trying to do daily tasks.

Physical therapists work in clinics, hospi-
tals, and schools for the handicapped. They
must be licensed to practice in all 50 states of
the United States.   W.R.P./J.J.F.

PIAGET, JEAN (1896-1980) Jean Piaget
(pyä zhā) was a Swiss psychologist who is
best known for his work in the field of child
psychology. He suggested the theory that a
child's mental abilities, like his physical
abilities, develop (grow) in a certain order
through a series of specific steps. The four
stages of development, as suggested by
Piaget, are sensory-motor, preoperational,
concrete operations, and formal operations.
In the sensory-motor stage (birth to 2 years
old), a child learns about objects, or things,
through the use of his senses—tasting,
smelling, hearing, seeing, and touching objects. In the preoperational stage (2 to 7 years

old), a child begins calling objects by their names. This is the beginning of language for the child. In the concrete operations stage (7 to 11 years old), a child begins to think logically. The child understands likenesses and differences which he uses in naming objects. The child has begun to think in an organized way. In the formal operations stage (11 years old to adulthood), the child begins to think abstractly. He can understand abstract words and concepts such as space, time, and freedom.

From the time he was a young child, Piaget was interested in science. He published a scientific paper when he was only 10 years old. He received a doctor's degree in science in 1918. Piaget used his interest in science for his work in psychology. He was among the first to take a biological approach to the development of mental abilities. His theories are widely accepted and respected throughout the world. *See also* PSYCHOLOGY. A.J.C./D.G.F.

PICCARD, AUGUSTE (1884–1962) August Piccard (pi kär′) was a Swiss scientist who was born in Basel. He had a twin brother, Jean Felix, who was also a scientist. In 1932, Auguste Piccard used a balloon to fly up to the stratosphere (an upper part of the atmosphere) to study cosmic rays. In order to go this high into the atmosphere, Piccard invented a pressurized cabin. He showed that flying at high altitudes was possible. Piccard reached an altitude of 16,050 m [52,657 ft].

In 1945, Piccard made a bathyscaphe to be able to study what happens to sunlight deep in the ocean. The bathyscaphe was a spherical steel cabin, built to protect him from the water pressure deep in the ocean. Piccard's bathyscaphe reached a depth of 11,000 m [35,800 ft]. *See also* BATHYSCAPHE; BATHYSPHERE.

C.M./D.G.F.

A model of Auguste Piccard's bathyscaphe *Trieste* is shown below. Aboard the *Trieste*, Piccard's son, Jacques, descended 11,000 m [35,800 ft] into the Pacific Ocean. The bathyscaphe protected him from the water pressure deep in the ocean.

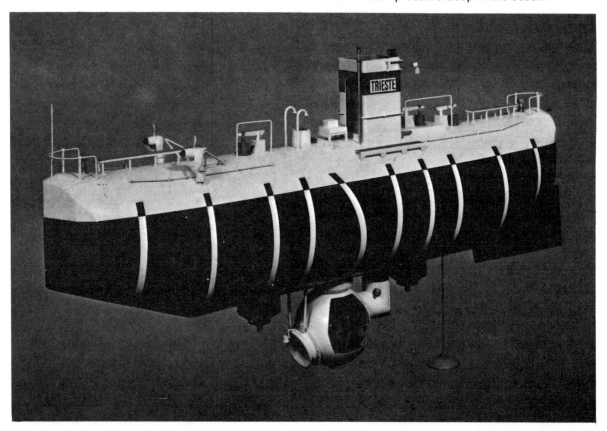

PICKEREL (pik′ ə rəl) A pickerel is a freshwater fish that belongs to the pike family Esocidae. (*See* PIKE.) There are three species of pickerel in North America: the grass, redfin, and chain pickerel. All of these fishes have long, slender bodies, long, pointed snouts, and many sharp teeth. They are greenish in color.

Pickerel live in shallow, weedy lakes or slow-moving rivers. They sit very still near a log or rock, waiting for a small animal to swim by. When one swims near, pickerel dart out very quickly and take the prey in their teeth. Pickerel eat small fish, frogs, snakes, and insects.

Redfin and grass pickerel rarely go beyond 30 cm [12 in] in length, so they are not often sought by fishermen. The chain pickerel, however, grows to lengths over 60 cm [24 in]. It is a popular game fish.

S.R.G./E.C.M.

PIEZOELECTRIC EFFECT (pē ā′ zō ə lek′ trik i fekt′) If certain crystals are pressed or stretched, an electric voltage develops across the crystal. This is called the piezoelectric effect. The crystal with the strongest piezoelectric effect is Rochelle's salt. If a voltage is applied to a piezoelectric crystal, the crystal expands or contracts. This is called the reverse piezoelectric effect.

Piezoelectric crystals have many uses. The expansion or contraction of a crystal can be used to produce sound waves. Therefore piezoelectric crystals are used to convert electric signals into sound waves and vice versa. For example, they are used in telephone mouthpieces to convert sound into an electric signal. In the earpiece of a telephone, the electric signal is converted back into sound by another piezoelectric signal. They are also used in microphones and in the pickup (which holds the needle) of record players.

Another important use for piezoelectric crystals is in sonar equipment. Sonar equipment is used on ships and submarines. Sonars make sound waves under the water. The waves are used to find underwater objects. The waves are produced by the vibrations of a piezoelectric crystal. If an object is present, the waves are reflected off the object. A piezoelectric crystal then picks up the reflected wave and turns it into an electric signal. In this way, objects under the water are displayed on a screen. (*See* SONAR.)

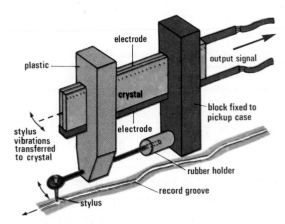

PIEZOELECTRIC PICKUP

In a record player pickup, which is a piezoelectric instrument, vibrations of the stylus in the grooves of the record cause the piezoelectric crystal to emit signals.

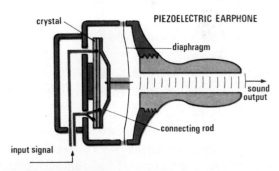

PIEZOELECTRIC EARPHONE

In a sound-producing earphone, electrical signals cause the piezoelectric crystal to vibrate, and sound waves are produced.

An alternating voltage is a voltage that varies. The voltage decreases in one direction to zero. Then it builds up in the opposite direction. It again decreases to zero and then increases in the original direction. If an alternating voltage is applied to a piezoelectric crystal, the crystal vibrates. It expands when the voltage goes in one direction. Then the crystal returns to normal as the voltage decreases to zero. The crystal contracts when the voltage goes in the opposite direction. The atoms in a crystal have a natural frequency of vibration. Frequency means the number of vibrations in a second. (*See* FREQUENCY.) If the frequency of the voltage is the same as the natural frequency of the crystal, then the crystal resonates. (*See* RESONANCE.) This means that it vibrates very strongly. This effect is used in radio broadcasting. The frequency of radio waves must be kept at a steady value. Quartz crystals are used for this purpose because they resonate at the required frequency. Quartz crystals are widely used in piezoelectric devices because they are very stable, even at high temperatures. M.E./L.L.R.

PIG (pig') Farmyard pigs, or hogs (also called swine) are descended from the wild boars that roamed throughout Asia, Europe, and north Africa several thousand years ago. Many scientists believe that people began taming pigs about 8,500 years ago. It is believed that such pigs were used as village scavengers. Pigs are omnivorous—they eat almost anything that is animal or vegetable. In the early 1500s, Spanish and French explorers brought domestic hogs to North and South America. The European wild boar (*Sus scrofa*) is the animal from which many domestic hogs are descended.

Until the 1940s, United States farmers classified hog breeds as one of two kinds— lard type or bacon type. Lard-type hogs had more fat in proportion to lean meat. Meatpacking plants made the fat into lard. This lard was used for cooking and other purposes. In the 1950s, shortening made from vegetable oils began to replace lard. Since then, farmers have raised hogs mainly for their meat. One of the most interesting aspects of pig-breeding has been the gradual shift of the pigs' weight from front to rear. Wild boars have heavy shoulders. But the best meat is on the hindquarters. Breeders have concentrated on selecting pigs with small shoulders and large back legs. (*See* BREEDING.)

Many different breeds of pigs have been developed in various parts of the world to meet local climate and pasture conditions. Farmers in the United States raise about 20 breeds of hogs. American Landrace, Tamworth, and Yorkshire pigs are raised mainly for bacon. Pigs that weigh from 91 to 104 kg [200 to 230 lb] have about the right amount of fat to produce good meat.

In modern farming practice, pigs are fed on a carefully balanced diet containing proteins, carbohydrates, and minerals. Such nutrients are provided by feeding the pigs corn and other grains, such as sorghum, barley, wheat, rye, and oats. About 1.8 kg [4 lb] of feed are needed to add 0.4 kg [1 lb] to a pig's weight.

A sow (adult female pig) gives birth to 8 to 20 piglets (baby pigs) at a time, two or three times a year. Pigs reproduce rapidly and can be mated when about eight months old. Sows carry their young about 114 days before they farrow (give birth). A piglet weighs about 1.1 kg [2.5 lb] at birth, but gains weight quickly, usually doubling its weight the first week. When it is only one year old, a piglet can weigh 113 kg [250 lb]. The average adult boar (male) weighs from 159 to 230 kg [350 to 500 lb]. The average adult sow weighs from 140 to 204 kg [300 to 450 lb]. Most pigs are marketed when they are about six or eight months old, weighing from 82 to 109 kg [180 to 240 lb]. Pigs kept beyond this age are usually used for breeding purposes.

The pig's snout has a flat, tough disk on the end that includes the nostrils. Hogs have canine teeth that develop into sharp tusks. These tusks serve as tools for digging and as weapons for fighting. They are much larger on males than on females. The pig has four

Pigs today, such as these, facing right, are bred for bacon and other pork meats.

toes on each foot. Each toe ends in a hoof.

Pork, ham, bacon, and spareribs all come from the meat of pigs. A pig's meat can be smoked or salted and then kept for a long time without spoiling. Pig intestines are used as the casing for sausages. Besides its use as food, the pig has other uses. The pig's hide, when tanned, becomes the leather known as pigskin. Pigskin is used to make such items as gloves and luggage. The stiff bristles from the pig's hide are made into paint brushes and hairbrushes. Pig blood is used in feed for animals, fertilizer, and medicine.

J.J.A./J.J.M.

A wild boar and its descendant, the domestic pig, are shown. Most of the boar's weight is in the front of the body, but the pig's weight is concentrated in the hind quarters. This change in shape is the result of selective breeding by farmers.

PIG IRON (pig′ īrn) Pig iron is the name for all iron made in blast furnaces. Coming from the blast furnace, pig iron is not pure iron. It usually contains about 95 percent iron, 3 or 4 percent carbon, and smaller amounts of other elements, such as sulfur, phosphorus, and manganese.

In a pig-casting machine, the molten (liquid) iron flows into molds. The term "pig" comes from an early method of running hot iron into sand molds arranged around a main channel like a litter of pigs around the mother.

Today, most pig iron is not cast into pigs, but is used to make steel. The molten iron is carried from the blast furnaces to "mixers," which are huge heated tanks. Mixers keep the iron in liquid form until it is used by the steel-making furnaces.

J.J.A./A.D.

Pig iron is cast into many small molds where it solidifies into masses called pigs.

PIGMENT (pig′ mənt) Pigment is a substance, often in the form of a powder, that gives color to another material. Pigment colors a material in one of two ways—it is mixed in with the material or applied over its surface in a thin layer.

Pigment does not dissolve, but remains suspended in a liquid. For example, when pigment is suspended in a liquid it may form paint. Colored substances that dissolve in liquids (giving color by staining) are called dyes. (*See* DYE.) Transparent pigments are often used to add bulk or to improve hardness or durability of paints.

Pigments also occur in nature. In biology, a pigment is any substance that colors the tissues or cells of animals or plants. (*See* PIGMENTATION.) *See also* ALBINO; COLOR; PAINT; SKIN.

J.J.A./E.R.L.

PIGMENTATION (pig' mən tā' shən) The coloring of a plant or an animal is nearly always caused by the presence of one or more pigments. These are colored substances in the cells of the outer layers of the plant or animal. Many animals, such as chameleons, cephalopods, and flatfish, can change their appearance by altering the distribution of pigments in their skin. Nerves or hormones cause the pigment granules to disperse or contract, thereby changing the color of the skin. (*See* CAMOUFLAGE.)

The main pigment in human coloration is melanin. This dark-colored pigment is found in the skin and hair. The color of skin is determined by the amount of this pigment. People from sunny regions, such as Africa, have large amounts of melanin and are dark brown or nearly black. The high melanin content has evolved in these races because it protects the underlying layers of skin from sunburn. People from cooler and less sunny regions have paler skins. But (with the exception of albinos) people always have melanin. People with light-colored skin can produce more melanin when their skin is exposed to extra sunlight. Their skin turns browner.

Melanin is also responsible for hair color. Dark hair contains much melanin. Blonde hair has only a little. Red-haired people, who often have pale skins, also have little melanin. *See also* ALBINO. J.J.A./C.R.N.

PIKA (pē' kə) The pika is a small, furry mammal closely related to the hare and rabbit. Pikas are found in Asia, Europe, and North America. The animals often live among loose rock on mountainsides. Some kinds of pikas live together in large groups called colonies.

The American pika (*Ochotona princeps*) is frequently called a conie or a calling hare. American pikas are about 18 cm [7 in] long, not including the tail. Their coat is grayish brown on the back with white or light brown covering the underside. American pikas resemble guinea pigs. Collared pikas

(*Ochotona collaris*) are also found in North America living in mountains farther north than the American pika.

Pikas feed on plants. The animals spend much time collecting grasses and herbs to use during the winter months. Pikas store these foods by stacking them in piles that look like small haystacks. *See also* HARE; RABBIT.

J.J.A./J.J.M.

PIKE (pīk') A pike is a freshwater fish that belongs to the family Esocidae. Its full name is the northern pike. The northern pike is found all over the world in northern lakes and sluggish rivers. It feeds similar to its close relative, the pickerel. (*See* PICKEREL.)

The northern pike is one of the most popular game fishes in North America. It has been widely stocked into waters in which it did not previously live. The largest pike caught by a North American fisherman was 20.9 kg [46 lb 2 oz] in weight. Pike are very strong fighters. *See also* MUSKELLUNGE. S.R.G./E.C.M.

PILING (pī' ling) Piling is a method of making a strong foundation for a building, bridge, or other large structure. Piling is used when the upper layers of soil are too weak to support an ordinary foundation.

Piles are usually columns of concrete or steel. When a skyscraper, suspension bridge, or other huge structure is to be built, a strong foundation is necessary. Often, the soil below the building site is weak, and the bedrock lies too far down to be reached. In such a case, huge pillars of reinforced concrete are sunk down to reach the rock. If the piles do not reach the rock, friction piles are used. Support comes from the adhesion between soil and pile. (*See* ADHESION.)

Sheet piles are used to support horizontal loads. Sheet piles usually consist of interlocking sheets of steel. They give the necessary support for the sides of temporary excavations, such as dam construction sites.

Various tools are used to place piles in the

ground. A pile driver drives a concrete pile into the ground. A steam hammer drives piles into the ground with steam pressure. The modern pneumatic hammer uses compressed air, while the drop hammer uses a diesel engine. A vibrating pile driver shakes a pile into the ground. *See also* BUILDING CONSTRUCTION. J.M.C./R.W.L.

PILOT FISH (pī′ lət fish′) The pilot fish is a saltwater fish that belongs to family Carangidae. It grows to a length of about 60 cm [24 in]. The pilot fish is found in the Pacific and Atlantic oceans. It is white or pale blue with dark vertical bands on its sides. It is called a pilot fish because it is always seen swimming near large fish and whales. It was once believed that the pilot fish guided the large animals to food. Ichthyologists—scientists who study fish—now believe that they swim near large fish because it is easier for them to swim in the currents caused by the large fish. *See also* ICHTHYOLOGY. S.R.G./E.C.M.

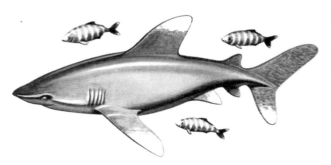

Pilot fish are shown swimming close to a shark.

PILTDOWN MAN (pilt′ daùn′ man′) Piltdown man was the name given to the fossil remains of a supposed prehistoric human being. The fossils were discovered in 1912 in a gravel pit at Piltdown, England. In 1955, the fossils were proven to be fake.

The fossils consisted of a skull and jawbone. The braincase seemed very modern, while the jaw was quite apelike. Analyses completed in the 1950s proved that the skull was of a human being who lived about 750

years ago. The jaw was that of a modern ape. The jaw had been stained by chemicals to appear older, and the teeth had been artificially ground down to render a human appearance.

For 40 years, Piltdown man caused an amazing scientific uproar. The hoax did, however, have the positive effect of stimulating the development of new methods of finding the age of fossils. *See also* DATING; FOSSIL. J.M.C./S.O.

PINEAL GLAND (pī′ nē əl gland′) The pineal gland is an endocrine gland found in vertebrates near the center of the brain. The role of this pea-sized gland is unclear. The pineal gland is thought to secrete (give off) the hormone melatonin. Melatonin has been found to affect the growth of the sex glands in some young animals. In certain adult animals, it seems to regulate the activity of the sex glands. In human beings, melatonin may determine when a person reaches sexual maturity. It may also help to regulate the menstrual cycle in sexually mature women.

Some scientists have suggested that the pineal is a vestigial sense organ. (*See* VESTIGIAL ORGAN.) However, the exact function of the pineal gland remains uncertain. *See also* ENDOCRINE; HORMONE; MENSTRUAL CYCLE. J.M.C./J.J.F.

PINEAPPLE (pī′ nap′ əl) The pineapple (*Ananas sativus*) is a fruit-bearing plant belonging to the bromeliad family (*Bromeliaceae*). The plant probably originated in Brazil. It is grown today in tropical areas throughout the world.

The pineapple plant grows to heights of 60 to 90 cm [2 to 3 ft]. Its leaves are sword-shaped and spiny. Purplish flowers grow in clusters on thick stalks. (*See* INFLORESCENCE.) Each of these flowers produces a small, fleshy fruitlet. These fruitlets fuse together to form one large fruit, the pineapple. The fruit weighs from 2 to 4 kg [4 to 6 lb]. Its firm flesh is a light yellow color. The group of leaves at the top of the fruit is called the crown. Although most pineapples have small brown seeds, a popular variety, called Smooth Cayenne, is seedless.

Pineapple plants require a warm climate and a moderate amount of water. The land needs to be well-tilled before planting. Chemicals are often spread over the land to prevent damage to the plants by parasitic nematodes. (*See* NEMATODE.) Plastic strips are sometimes laid down to help the soil retain nutrients and water.

Nearly one-third of the pineapples produced each year are cultivated in Hawaii. Some important pineapple-producing countries are Brazil, Malaysia, and Mexico. *See also* FRUIT. J.M.C./M.H.S.

The pineapple plant is grown today in tropical areas throughout the world.

PINE FAMILY The pine (pīn′) family includes 10 genera and more than 250 species of coniferous trees. They have needlelike leaves that grow in small clusters or in spirals around the stem. The male and the female reproductive structures are in different cones on the same plant. (*See* MONOECIOUS.)

Pine trees are more than 100 species of evergreen conifers that belong to genus *Pinus*. They are found throughout the world, mostly in the northern hemisphere. Huge forests of pine trees grow across Canada and the northern United States.

There are two types of pine trees: soft, or white, pines; and hard, or yellow, pines. The soft pines include the largest and the oldest pines. The sugar pines of California and Oregon sometimes grow to a height of 75 m [248 ft]. The bristlecone pines are among the oldest living trees. Some are almost 5,000 years old and are still alive. The hard pines include some of the most valuable lumber trees in North America.

Pine trees provide a fine lumber that is important in the construction, furniture, and paper industries. (*See* LUMBER.) They are also sources of oil, turpentine, charcoal, and fuel gases (by-products produced by distillation). Other members of the pine family include cedar, Douglas fir, fir, hemlock, larch, and spruce. *See also* CONIFER; EVERGREENS; GYMNOSPERM. A.J.C./M.H.S.

Young, female cones of a pine tree are pictured.

After growing for two years, female pine cones are hard and woody.

PINK FAMILY The pink (pingk) family includes 75 genera with more than 2,000 species of herbaceous plants. They are dicotyledons and grow throughout the world. (*See* DICOTYLEDON.) The leaves grow in opposite pairs, and have smooth margins. (*See* LEAF.) The stem is swollen at the nodes, the points of leaf attachment. (*See* NODE.) The flowers usually grow in clusters.

Genus *Gypsophila* includes 50 species known as baby's breath. These plants produce tiny pink or white flowers which are often added to bouquets of other flowers as trim. The most popular members of the pink family belong to genus *Dianthus*. This genus includes the carnations, sweet williams, and pinks.   A.J.C./M.H.S.

A garden pink, of the pink family, is shown.

PIPEFISH (pīp′ fish′) A pipefish is a thin, snakelike, saltwater fish that belongs to the family Syngnathidae. It is related to the sea horse. (*See* SEA HORSE.) The strange-looking pipefish lives in the shallow coastal waters of the Atlantic and Pacific oceans. There are 21 species in North America. Pipefish eat plankton. (*See* PLANKTON.) S.R.G./E.C.M.

PIPETTE (pī pet′) A pipette is a piece of glass apparatus used in chemistry. It is used for transferring an exact volume of a liquid from one container to another. It is used regularly in quantitative analysis. (*See* CHEMICAL ANALYSIS.) In quantitative analysis, the quantities of substances used must be accurate.

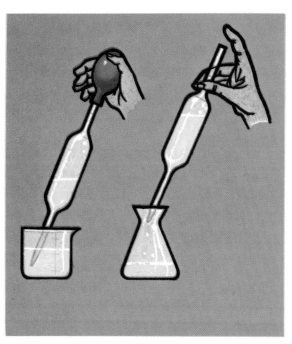

A large pipette is being used to measure out an exact volume of liquid. The aspirating bulb is used to draw up liquid into the narrow neck, where a line shows the exact measure. The bulb is removed, and the liquid is released into a flask.

A pipette consists of a cylindrical glass bulb. At each end of the bulb there is a length of thin glass tubing. The lower end of the pipette has a thin tip. This is placed in the liquid. The liquid is then sucked up the pipette until it fills the bulb and part of the upper glass tube. If the liquid is poisonous or corrosive, a rubber bulb is used for this. Otherwise the liquid is sucked up by the mouth. The upper tube has a line marked on it. The pipette is filled to a point above this line. Then a finger is placed over the top of the pipette. This prevents the liquid from running back out of the pipette. When the pressure of the finger is relaxed just a little, the liquid runs out of the tube very slowly. When the liquid reaches the line, the pressure of the finger is increased. This stops the liquid from running out any more. The pipette now holds an exact volume of the liquid. This can be transferred to another container.

There are different sizes of pipettes for measuring different volumes of a liquid.

M.E./R.W.L.

PIRANHA (pə ran′ yə) A piranha is a freshwater fish that belongs to the family Characidae. It is a very fierce fish with a mouth full of razor-sharp teeth. A piranha is capable of biting a person's finger off. It is found in the Amazon River of South America, where piranhas live in schools of hundreds of fish. When an animal falls into the river, these schools of piranhas can eat everything but the bones in a matter of minutes. Piranhas grow only as long as 60 cm [24 in]. They are often kept in the United States as aquarium pets, although it is illegal to do so in some states because of the danger of their being released or introduced into our warm water rivers. *See also* AQUARIUM.

S.R.G./E.C.M.

PISCES (pī′ sēz) Pisces is the zodiac constellation located between Aries and Aquarius. It is visible from the mid-northern hemisphere between September and January.

Pisces is a very faint constellation. Its brightest stars are only of fourth and fifth magnitude. The sun is in Pisces at the vernal equinox, about March 21.

Pisces was named for two fish. According to Greek myths, the gods Aphrodite and Eros transformed themselves into fish to escape an evil monster. *See also* CONSTELLATION; EQUINOX; ZODIAC.

J.M.C./C.R.

PISTIL (pis′ təl) The pistil is the female reproductive structure of a flower. It usually has three parts: stigma, style, and ovary. The stigma is at the top of the pistil. It has a sticky surface that will hold any pollen grains that land on it. (*See* POLLINATION.) The stigma leads to a tubelike style which opens into the ovary. In some plants, the style is missing, and the stigma is directly on top of the ovary. It is in the ovary that ovules (eggs) are produced and fertilized. (*See* OVARY.)

The number of pistils in a flower varies by species. Some flowers have many pistils; some have none. Some flowers have a compound pistil—actually several pistils fused into one. *See also* FLOWER; FRUIT.

A.J.C./M.H.S.

PITCH (pich′) Pitch is a black, gluelike substance that is left behind when petroleum or coal tar is distilled. It is called asphalt in its natural form. Pitch is water repellent and highly adhesive. It is used for roof coatings, highway paving, and waterproofing applications. *See also* ASPHALT; DISTILLATION.

W.R.P./J.M.

PITCHBLENDE (pich′ blend′) Pitchblende is an important ore of the radioactive metal uranium. It occurs in igneous rocks, mainly granite, and in veins of iron, copper, lead, and tin minerals. Pitchblende is usually brown, black, or dark gray. It consists mainly of the compound uranium oxide. It also contains small amounts of other elements such as radium, thorium, and zirconium. *See also* URANINITE.

M.E./R.H.

PITOT TUBE (pē′ tō′ tüb′) A pitot tube is used for measuring the rate at which a gas or a liquid flows. For example, a pitot tube can be placed inside a pipeline. In this case it measures the rate at which a gas or a liquid flows through the pipeline. A pitot tube can also be fitted onto an airplane. It measures the speed of the air flowing past the airplane. This tells

Pitot tubes are often fitted to airplanes to measure airspeed. On this autogiro, a pitot tube is fitted to one wing (see inside black circle). The nozzles of the pitot tube (two, on this model) point in the direction of the autogiro's movement through the air. Two different air pressures are measured: the dynamic pressure of the air thrusting into the tubes, and the static pressure of the air on the inside walls of the tubes. From these two pressures, the airspeed is calculated. In an airplane this is done automatically, and airspeed is recorded on a dial in the cockpit.

the pilot how fast he is moving relative to the rate of flow of the air. This is called the air speed of the airplane.

The pitot tube was invented by a French engineer, Henri Pitot, during the 1700s. A pitot tube is a narrow metal tube that is bent at a right angle. One end has a nozzle that faces into the fluid flow. Since the tube is small, it hardly disturbs the flow. If it did, then its measurements would not be accurate. In pipelines, the other end of the pitot tube is connected to a manometer. A manometer is an instrument that measures differences in pressure. (*See* MANOMETER.) The reading on this manometer is due to two different sorts of pressure in the pitot. One is called the dynamic pressure. This is caused by the gas or liquid moving through the pitot. There is also static pressure. This is the pressure exerted by the fluid even when it is not flowing. To calculate the rate of flow, only the dynamic

pressure is needed. Therefore, the static pressure must be subtracted from the reading on the manometer. The static pressure is measured by another manometer. Then the rate of flow can be calculated.

Basically the same method is used for measuring air speeds. Usually the airplane contains equipment that automatically calculates the air speed and gives a direct reading on a dial. *See also* BERNOULLI'S EFFECT.

M.E./R.W.L.

PITUITARY GLAND *See* HORMONE.

PIT VIPER (pit vī′ pər) Pit vipers are poisonous snakes that belong to the viper family Crotalidae. The pit vipers get their name from the two pits—or shallow holes—that are found between their eyes and nostrils. These pits are sensitive to heat. They help the snakes locate warm-blooded prey such as small mammals. There are many pit vipers in Europe and Asia. Rattlesnakes, copperheads, and cottonmouths are the only pit vipers in

The piranha (facing left) is a fierce fish. Piranhas are abundant in rivers of eastern and central South America.

North America. The only other poisonous snake in North America is the coral snake. (*See* CORAL SNAKE.) *See also* COPPERHEAD; COTTONMOUTH; RATTLESNAKE; SNAKE.

S.R.G./R.L.L.

PLACENTA (plə sent′ ə) The placenta is a membrane that is formed during pregnancy to allow substances to be exchanged between blood of the mother and the embryo (the unborn young). Among all the members of the animal kingdom, only mammals have a placenta. The only mammals that do not develop a placenta are the pouched marsupials and the egg-laying monotremes. (*see* MARSUPIAL, MONOTREME.)

In the placenta, the blood of the embryo comes very close to, but never mixes with, the blood of the mother. Digested food, water, and oxygen pour out from the mother's blood into the embryo's blood. Waste products pour out from the embryo's blood into the mother's blood. In a sense then, the mother eats, breathes, and removes wastes for her unborn child.

The placenta forms from tissues surrounding the embryo and from some of the tissues in the mother's uterus. The placenta develops small, finger-like villi, which are bathed directly in the mother's blood. Blood flows

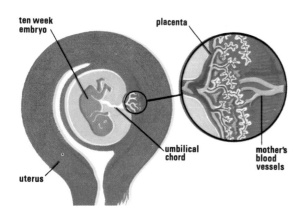

In its mother's uterus (womb) the embryo feeds, respires and excretes via the placenta, which is connected to the embryo by the umbilical cord and is separated only by a membrane from the mother's blood vessels.

through the umbilical cord to and from the villi. (*See* UMBILICAL CORD.) The umbilical cord connects the embryo to the placenta. In human beings, the placenta is almost fully formed within the first two months of pregnancy. Throughout the pregnancy, the placenta also makes hormones which are needed for the pregnancy to keep happening normally. Soon after the baby is born, the placenta is given off along with other membranes, all of which is called the afterbirth. However, some mammals do not force out the placenta, they take it back into their systems.

In flowering plants, the placenta is part of the ovary that is attached to fertilized ovules (eggs) as they develop into seeds. It gives food to the seed. *See also* EMBRYO, PREGNANCY.

A.J.C./J.J.F.

PLAICE *See* FLATFISH.

PLANCK, MAX (1858–1947) (plängk′) Max Planck was a German physicist. He was born at Kiel, where his father was a professor. In Berlin, Max Planck was a student of Gustav Kirchhoff and Hermann Helmholtz. Kirchhoff's ideas may have sparked Planck's interest in radiation.

Planck is famous for developing the quantum theory. In 1901, he said that energy behaves as if it is in tiny bits. He called these bits of energy quanta. At first, this idea was believed to be so new and different that it was not taken seriously. Gradually, scientists realized that the quantum theory helped to explain things they could not explain any other way. They had believed that energy always moved in waves. Today, both wave and quantum theories are used to explain what we can see. One of the most important theories based on the quantum theory is Niels Bohr's atomic theory.

In 1918, Planck was awarded the Nobel Prize for physics. *See also* ATOM; BOHR, NIELS; KIRCHHOFF, GUSTAV; LIGHT; PHOTON; QUANTUM THEORY.

C.M./D.G.F.

PLANCK'S CONSTANT (plängks′ kän′ stənt) Light, X rays, and radio waves are all examples of electromagnetic radiation. (*See* ELECTROMAGNETIC RADIATION.) Electromagnetic radiation sometimes acts as if it were made up of waves. At other times it acts as if it were made up of particles. These particles are called photons. (*See* PHOTON.) Electromagnetic radiation can have different frequencies. For example, X rays have a higher frequency than light. This means that X rays vibrate more times per second than light vibrates. The energy of a photon of electromagnetic radiation is called a quantum. (*See* QUANTUM THEORY.) It is proportional to the frequency of the photon. This means that the energy equals the frequency multiplied by a constant number. This constant is called Planck's constant. It is named after its discoverer, the German physicist Max Planck. (*See* PLANCK, MAX.) Planck's constant is written as h and is equal to 6.626×10^{-34} joule-seconds. (10^{-34} is 1 divided by 10 thirty-four times.) A joule is a unit of energy. *See also* JOULE.

M.E./J.D.

PLANE FAMILY The plane (plān′) family consists of one genus (*Platanus*) with 10

The plane tree grows equally well in the country and in towns and cities.

species of large, deciduous trees that are native to temperate areas of North America, Europe, and Asia. (*See* DECIDUOUS TREE.) The members of this family have large, palmately lobed (resembling a hand with fingers spread) leaves. (*See* LEAF.) Each plant has both male flowers and female flowers. (See MONOECIOUS.) Though separate, they are closely grouped in thick round heads. The fruit is a knobby ball that has many seeds.

The American sycamore (*Platanus occidentalis*) is the largest member of the plane family. It sometimes reaches a height of more than 50 m [165 ft]. *See also* SYCAMORE.

A.J.C./M.H.S.

PLANET

In astronomy, a planet (plan′ət) is a body that revolves around a star. A planet gives off no light of its own. It can be seen because it reflects light from the star. It also receives most of its heat from the star. Depending on its size and mass, a planet is said to be major or minor. A minor planet is usually called an asteroid. A planet is distinct from a comet, which also orbits a star, by having a metal or rock core. (*See* ASTEROID; COMET; STAR.)

Solar system   There are nine known planets in orbit around the sun. (*See* ORBIT; SUN.) In the order of increasing size of their orbits, they are Mercury, Venus, Earth, Mars, Jupiter, Saturn, Uranus, Neptune, and Pluto. Except for Mercury and Pluto, they orbit in approximately the same plane.

A planet may be orbited by one or more smaller, solid bodies called satellites, or moons. Seven of the nine planets of the solar system are known to have moons. (*See* SATELLITE.)

Astronomers think that other stars in the universe may be orbited by one or more planets. In 1983 they found evidence that a star called Vega has a solar system of its own. But the tremendous distance from earth of this and other stars makes the search for other planets very difficult. (*See* GALAXY.)

When viewed from the earth, planets appear to be stars. Planets seem to give off a steady light, while stars twinkle. Because planets are relatively near earth, their motion against the background of stars is noticeable. Because the stars are so distant, they appear to remain in the same relative position. Actually, the stars are moving thousands of times faster than any of the planets.

The planets are divided into two groups: the inner, or terrestrial, planets and the outer, or Jovian, planets. The inner planets—Mercury, Venus, Earth, Mars—are similar in size and have a solid, rocky surface. The outer planets resemble Jupiter (hence, Jovian) in consisting largely of gases. All the outer planets are large except for Pluto, which is about the size of the earth's moon.

Pluto and Neptune are too far from earth to be seen without a telescope. The other planets can be seen in the night sky. Mercury, because of its closeness to the sun, is visible only briefly after sunset or before sunrise.

Planet movements Each planet follows an elliptical orbit around the sun. As it orbits (or revolves), it turns, or rotates, on its axis. The closer a planet is to the sun, the less time it takes for it to complete its orbit. Mercury completes its orbit in 88 days. Pluto, the most distant planet, takes 248 years. All the planets orbit in the same direction.

The closer a planet is to the sun, the faster its orbital speed. Mercury, the closest, has a velocity of 48 km per second [30 mi per second]. Pluto, the farthest, travels at 4.7 km per sec [2.7 mi per sec]. The earth's velocity is about 12.8 km per sec [8 mi per sec, about 28,500 mph].

Of the terrestrial planets, earth rotates on its axis once every 24 hours. Mercury takes 59 days, Venus takes 243 days, Mars takes 24 hours and 37 minutes, and Pluto takes 6 days, 9 hours, and 18 minutes. The Jovian planets show less variation, ranging from about 10 to 18 hours. Venus and Uranus rotate clockwise. The other seven planets rotate counterclockwise.

All the planets except Mercury have a tilted axis. No two planets rotate on the same tilt. The earth's axis is tilted about 24°. Uranus is tilted about 98°.

The planets differ greatly in mass and density, and therefore also in gravity. The density of Saturn and Pluto is less than that of water. The density of the other Jovian planets is slightly more than that of water. The largest of the Jovian planets, Jupiter, has 318 times the mass of earth. The surface gravity of a planet depends on its diameter and its mass. A person who weighs 54 kg [120 lb] on earth would weigh 21 kg [46 lb] on Mercury or Mars, 49 kg [109 lb] on Venus, and 138 kg [304 lb] on Jupiter.

Properties of the planets The characteristics of the planets are due in part to their distance from the sun. The planets closer to the sun have higher temperatures than the more distant planets. A planet's atmosphere also affects how much of the sun's light and heat is absorbed.

Of all the planets, Mercury orbits closest to the sun, but its distance varies from 47 million to 69 million km [29 million to 43 million mi]. Mercury has no atmosphere. The temperature on its surface reaches about 400°C [752°F] during the day. At night, the temperature falls to below −150°C [−230°F]. One day on Mercury is equal to 30 earth days. Photographs of Mercury's surface taken by Mariner 10 in 1974-75 show it to be crater-marked rock. In composition, Mercury seems to be more like our moon than like any of the other planets. There is no evidence that Mercury ever had an atmosphere or lakes and rivers.

This photograph of the earth was taken from the *Apollo 11* spacecraft. Most of Africa and parts of Europe and Asia can be seen. The spacecraft was about 181,500 km (112,775 mi) away from the earth when the picture was taken.

During Project Apollo, astronauts reached the moon. A lunar module is pictured descending onto the moon's surface.

three hours after sunset or the three hours before sunrise.

The earth is unlike the other planets in many ways. It is apparently the only planet that can sustain life as we know it. Earth is the only planet with an oxygen-rich atmosphere. (*See* EARTH.)

Earth's other neighboring planet is Mars, barely more than half its size. A coating of dust stained by iron oxide gives the planet a reddish appearance when viewed through a telescope. Most of its surface is covered by desert terrain. Temperatures vary from near 21°C [70°F] at noon to about −100°C [−150°F] at midnight. There is a small amount of water on Mars, mostly in the form of ice caps at the north and south poles. Mars has a very thin atmosphere, which includes a trace of water vapor. Atmospheric pressure is so low that frozen water vaporizes rather than melts. Astronomers think the cap at the south pole may be mostly frozen carbon dioxide (dry ice). Its surface is dotted with huge volcanoes that were active when the planet was young. Space probes and satellites have revealed traces of erosion like that caused either by floods or by rivers, but no sign of life has been found.

Jupiter, Saturn, Uranus, and Neptune are all much larger than any of the other planets. But all are much less dense, being for the most part balls of gas—mainly helium and hydrogen. They all spin much more rapidly on their axes than the smaller planets. Jupiter rotates in less than 10 earth hours; all sides of the planet can be observed by telescope during a single night. Jupiter, Saturn, and Uranus are orbited by one or more wheeling rings. Jupiter's thin ring consists mainly of dust particles. Saturn has seven rings, made up of particles and blocks of frozen gas, rock, and water ice. Uranus has nine semitransparent rings. Because its axis is tipped more than 90°, Uranus does not have days and nights. Instead, each orbit consists of 42 years of sunlight followed by 42 years of darkness for

Venus was once thought to be much like earth. Space probes, however, have found it to be very different. The planet is surrounded by a cloud of sulfuric acid. Beneath the clouds, lightning flashes constantly, but no rain falls. The atmosphere is so dense that one could almost swim in it. The planet orbits in a nearly perfect circle, but it rotates clockwise, so the sun appears to rise in the west. There are three layers of clouds that act as a blanket. A clear atmosphere of carbon dioxide extends from the surface to the bottom cloud layer (32 km, 19.9 mi). The planet's temperature is about the same as the boiling point of sulfur, 425°C [800°F]. There is little difference in temperature anywhere on the planet. A day on Venus is equal to 243 earth days. There is no measurable magnetic field, no weather, and no seasonal change.

Venus is the closest planet to the earth, and it is the brightest object in the night sky other than the moon. It is often called the Evening Star. Venus is usually visible in the

any point on the planet's surface.

Like the Jovian planets, Pluto is very cold compared to earth. Astronomers think its surface temperature is near absolute zero. Its orbit is so far from the sun that it takes 248 earth years to complete one revolution. Its orbit crosses that of Neptune, but there is no possibility that the two planets could collide because their orbits are in different planes.

A space probe launched by the United States in April 1973 (Pioneer 11) flew by Jupiter in December 1974 and reached Saturn in September 1979. In 1983 it passed out of the solar system. Astronomers hope to learn more about the planets with the help of orbiting telescopes. *See also* OBSERVATORY; TELESCOPE.   P.G.Z./G.D.B.

PLANETARIUM (plan′ ə ter′ ē əm) A planetarium is a model or device that shows the positions and movements of certain heavenly bodies.

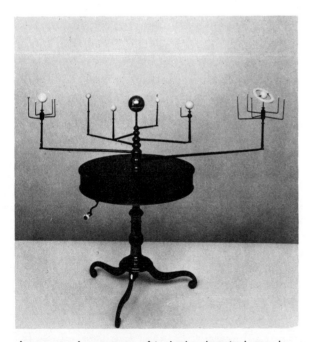

An orrery, forerunner of today's planetariums, is pictured above. The sun is represented by the central ball. The outer balls, which can be rotated, represent the planets. Small balls surrounding the planets represent moons.

The oldest type of planetarium is called an orrery. An orrery is a mechanical device which represents the sun as a large ball, the planets as slightly smaller balls, and moons as still smaller balls. These balls can be rotated to portray planetary movements. (*See* PLANET.)

Many museums and universities have planetariums where projectors are used to throw an image of the night sky on a domed ceiling. In this way, the sky of the southern hemisphere or the skies during the different seasons can be shown. The projectionist, often an astronomer, may give a lecture describing the projection and discuss a wide range of astronomical phenomena. The auditorium or building which has a solar system projector is also called a planetarium. *See also* ASTRONOMY.   J.M.C./C.R.

PLANKTON (plang′ tən) Plankton is the mass of small, floating organisms that live in bodies of water. It is made up of both animals (zooplankton) and plants (phytoplankton). Most of the zooplankton consists of small animals such as protozoans, fish eggs and larvae, and tiny crustaceans. It sometimes includes larger animals such as jellyfish. Most of the phytoplankton is small plants such as algae. Phytoplankton accounts for most of the world's photosynthesis and releases large amounts of oxygen into the air. (*See* PHOTOSYNTHESIS.)

Some planktonic organisms, such as algae, spend their entire lives as plankton. Others, such as fish eggs and larvae, are part of plankton only until they are developed enough to swim off on their own. While most of the plankton moves helplessly with the currents, some species of zooplankton are able to swim about on their own. (*See* NEKTON.)

Plankton is a major source of food for many larger aquatic animals. As such, it is an important part of the aquatic food chain. (*See* FOOD CHAIN.) Many scientists believe that, in the near future, plankton may be cultivated as a major source of food for human beings. (*See* DIET; FOOD.) *See also* BENTHOS.

A.J.C./R.J.B.

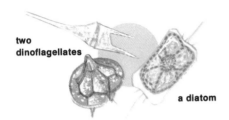

Single-celled plants of the plankton are shown above. The dinoflagellates are among the organisms which cause phosphorescence in seawater.

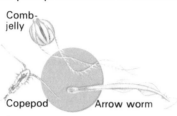

Three of the many kinds of animals found in plankton are illustrated above.

PLANTAIN FAMILY The plantain (plant′ ən) family includes three genera (plural of genus) and about 265 species of small, herbaceous plants and shrubs. They are dicotyledons (plants with two seed leaves) and are found all over the world. The leaves are simple, fleshy, and are arranged in opposite pairs. They usually grow in a rosette on the ground. From the middle of the rosette grows a leafless stalk. At the end of this stalk is a spike of tiny, green flowers. (*See* INFLORESCENCE.)

Common plantain (*Plantago major*) is a well-known plant that is often thought to be a weed when it grows in lawns. Its flowers make tiny, nutlike fruits which are a popular food for birds. (*See* DISPERSION OF PLANTS.)

The tropical plant that is called plantain looks like and is related to the banana. (*See* BANANA.) It is not related to the plantain family.

A.J.C./M.H.S.

PLANT DISEASE (plant′ diz ēz′) A plant disease is anything that kills, weakens, or otherwise affects the normal growth of a plant. The greatest danger of plant diseases is that they will destroy plants that are necessary for people to live. A serious outbreak of a plant disease can cause a famine— widespread lack of food that often causes the starvation and death of hundreds or thousands of people.

The causes of plant diseases can be divided into two major categories: non-living causes and living causes. Non-living causes include physical injury, chemical injury, and environmental factors. Some of the important environmental factors are temperature, water, light, air, and minerals. If the temperature is very high or low, or changes quickly, it will affect, and possibly kill, the plant. Plants need a certain amount of water to grow. Too little water can cut down the turgor pressure (the normal state of tension) in the cells and cause wilting. (*See* OSMOSIS; WILTING.) It can also stop or slow down the process of photosynthesis, sometimes causing the plant to "starve" to death. Too much water, however, can "drown" the roots, killing the plant. Floods or sudden, severe storms can kill plants or help the growth of other diseases which are caused by microorganisms. Air is important to the roots and to photosynthetic tissues. If the air is polluted, it may injure the plant. Certain chemical elements must be in the soil for a plant to grow properly. Some chemical elements, which are needed in fairly large amounts, are called macronutrients (the prefix "macro" means large). Micronutrients (the prefix "micro" means small) are needed in smaller amounts. If certain amounts of these chemicals are not in the soil, plant disease may occur. Many times, farmers and gardeners increase the minerals in the soil by adding fertilizers. (*See* FERTILIZER.)

The living causes of plant disease are fungi, bacteria, algae, viruses, insects, nematodes, and parasitic plants. Most plant diseases are caused by parasitic fungi. (*See* FUNGUS.) When a fungus spore lands on a

Barley smut and potato blight, as shown above, are two plant diseases which can seriously affect the food supply of humans.

plant tissue, it grows hyphae into the plant. These hyphae feed on the host's cells. When the fungus grows, it makes more spores. These spores are spread to other plants by the wind or other kinds or dispersion. (*See* DIS-PERSION OF PLANTS.) Some main fungus diseases are blight, mildew, rust, and smut.

There are more than 170 known types of parasitic bacteria that cause diseases in plants. (*See* BACTERIA.) These bacteria are usually carried by insects from plant to plant. They destroy plant cells in order to get food for themselves. Only a few types of algae cause plant disease. Most of these are found in the tropics, and do not usually cause important damage.

Viruses cause many plant diseases. (*See* VIRUS.) One of the most harmful is the tobacco mosaic virus which attacks tobacco and other members of the nightshade family. These viruses may be spread by touch or carried by insects and other animals. Insects cause great damage to plants. Insects carry harmful microorganisms, and they also eat and kill many plants. (*See* INSECT.) Nematodes are very small, wormlike animals that sometimes live as parasites on plants. (*See* NEMATODE.) There are more than 100 species of nematodes which attack every type of plant crop. Although they usually hurt the plant's roots, sometimes they hurt or kill the part of the plant above the ground.

There are many signs of plant disease. These include changes in leaf color; holes in the leaves; enlarged areas on the stem, roots, or leaves; stunted growth (the plant stops growing); falling off or death of parts (flowers, fruits, leaves) of the plant; or the death of the entire plant.

Plant diseases can often be held off by biological or chemical means. (*See* BIOLOGI-CAL CONTROL; FUNGICIDE; INSECTICIDE; PES-TICIDE.) They may also be fought by growing different crops or by breeding plants which can hold off some kinds of diseases. (*See* BREEDING.) *See also* AGRONOMY; DISEASE; GENETICS; MICROORGANISM; PATHOLOGY.

A.J.C./M.H.S.

PLANT KINGDOM

Plant kingdom (plant′ king′ dəm) is a group classification that includes all living and extinct (no longer in existence, not living) plants. Taxonomists are people who classify all living organisms (living beings made up of organs) in one of five kingdoms. (*See* KING-DOM.) The members of the plant kingdom have many cells and are chlorophyll-containing organisms. Other organisms (such as bacteria, fungi, and one-celled chlorophyll-containing organisms) which were once classified as plants are now placed in separate kingdoms. (*See* CLASSIFICATION OF LIVING ORGANISMS.)

How plants differ from animals   Plants are different from animals in many ways. Plants are able to make their own food by a process called photosynthesis. In order to make their food, plant cells have chlorophyll, a green color that "traps" some of the energy from sunlight. (*See* PHOTOSYNTHESIS.) Although most plants make more than enough food for themselves, some must depend on other organisms for part of their food. (*See* PARASITE; SAPROPHYTE.) However, all animals must depend on other organisms for their food. Some animals eat just plants and are called herbivores. Some animals eat only other animals and are called carnivores. Omnivores are animals that eat both plants and other animals.

In photosynthesis, plants use carbon dioxide from the air and water from the soil to make food (glucose) and oxygen. The food is either stored or used by the plant. The oxygen is given off into the air. Animals, however, use food and oxygen to make carbon dioxide and water. (*See* RESPIRATION.)

Most plants stay fixed in one place for their entire lives. Certain parts of the plant may move, but the plant itself does not move. (*See* MOVEMENT OF PLANTS.) Most animals, however, are able to move from one place to another under their own power.

It is possible for the growth of plants to be almost unlimited. The growth of a plant is usually held down by outside causes such as how much water, minerals, and sunlight are available. Animals, however, are usually limited in size—they will not grow beyond a certain size.

A plant cell is different from an animal cell. (*See* CELL.) Both the plant cell and animal cell have many similar structures. The plant cell, however, has a thick wall that has cellulose in it. Plant cells also have tiny structures that include pigments, or colors. Some of these tiny structures include chlorophyll. Others include other pigments such as carotene and xanthophyll.

Kinds of plants   There are several hundred thousand different species of plants. They are divided into two subkingdoms. Members of the subkingdom Thallophyta do not have any special structures that carry food, water, or minerals. They do not have true roots, stems, or leaves. Members of the subkingdom Embryophyta all grow from an embryo. (*See* EMBRYO.) Most embryophytes have roots, stems, and leaves. They also have special structures for moving food, water, and minerals from one part of the plant to another part of the plant.

The thallophytes include several phyla (plural of phylum: a division of the plant kingdom) of algae. (*See* ALGAE.) The simplest of these—the blue-green algae—are usually classified in kingdom Protista. The other types of algae are classified by color. Phylum Chrysophyta includes yellow-green and golden-brown algae. Phylum Pyrrophyta includes the algae commonly called dinoflagellates. Phylum Chlorophyta includes green algae. Phylum Phaeophyta includes brown algae. Phylum Rhodophyta includes red algae.

Most types of algae live in the water. Some, however, live in damp places on or near the ground. Algae make up most of the phytoplankton in the oceans. (*See* PLANKTON.) These algae account for nearly 75 percent of all the photosynthesis that happens on earth.

There are only two phyla of embryophytes: Bryophyta and Tracheophyta. The bryophytes are the simplest of the embryophytes. They do not have true roots, stems, or leaves. They do, however, have

The Evolution of Plants

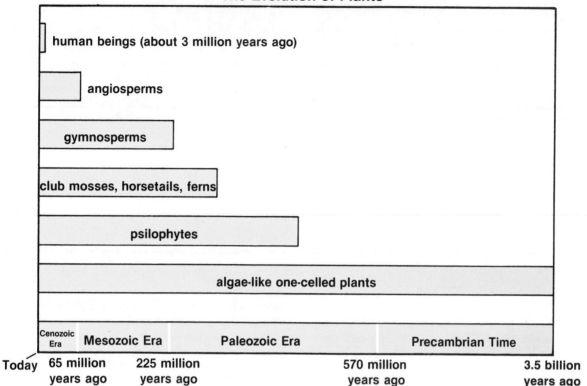

The graph above shows the evolution of plants from 3.5 billion years ago to today. Scientists believe the first plants lived in the oceans.

primitive structures—structures that have not changed since the plant first existed—that act like roots, stems, and leaves. They grow throughout the world in moist places. Bryophytes undergo alternation of generations—when two or more differently made forms happen in the life cycle of a plant. (*See* MOSS AND LIVERWORT.)

The tracheophytes have special tissues for carrying food, water, and minerals. (*See* VASCULAR PLANT.) The tracheophytes include psilophytes, club mosses, horsetails, ferns, gymnosperms, and angiosperms. The psilophytes were probably the first land plants. Though most are extinct, a few varieties still exist. (*See* PSILOPHYTE.)

Club mosses and horsetails were common prehistoric plants. Some grew as tall as modern-day trees. They descended (passed) from the psilophytes and were the first true vascular plants—plants with vessels for holding or carrying a liquid. (*See* CLUB MOSS; HORSETAIL.) Ferns are also simple vascular plants that were common in prehistoric times. Today, most ferns are small, rarely growing taller than 1 m [3.3 ft]. Some tropical varieties, however, grow taller than 12 m [40 ft]. (*See* FERN.)

The gymnosperms are seed-making plants that do not have flowers. (*See* GYMNOSPERM.) Most gymnosperms have seeds in cones. Gymnosperms are found throughout the world in almost every type of climate. The gymnosperms include conifers, cycads, ginkgoes, and gnetales. Most conifers are evergreen trees and shrubs with needlelike leaves. The cycads have large cones and fernlike leaves. The ginkgoes are conifers with fernlike leaves. All but one species are now extinct. The gnetales are three genera of plants with qualities of both gymnosperms and angiosperms.

The angiosperms are the flowering plants.

(*See* ANGIOSPERM.) They are the most highly evolved, or developed, members of the plant kingdom. Most of the plants in the world today are angiosperms. They show great variety in size, appearance, and ways of life. Most live on land. Some, however, live in fresh water. (*See* AQUATIC PLANT.) Some live in salt water. (*See* HALOPHYTE.) Some live in the air. (*See* EPIPHYTE.) Some live in hot, dry, desert areas. (*See* XEROPHYTE.) Some plants live in icy, Arctic regions. (*See* CRYOPHYTE.) Angiosperms are divided into two subclasses according to the structure of the seed that is made. The monocotyledons have seeds with one cotyledon. (*See* MONOCOTYLEDON.) The dicotyledons have seeds with two cotyledons. (*See* DICOTYLEDON.)

Structure of a flowering plant Flowering plants have vegetative structures (roots, stems, leaves) and reproductive structures (flowers, fruits, seeds). The roots hold the plant in the ground, and soak up water and liquid minerals from the soil. (*See* ROOT.) A plant may have a tap root or fibrous roots. A tap root is one large root that usually stores food and other nutrients (something that helps growth). Fibrous roots are many branching roots, all of which are about the same size. The roots of some aerial plants, such as epiphytes, hang in the air, soaking up water and nutrients from the air. Most parasitic and saprophytic plants have specialized roots called haustoria. The haustoria grow into a host (a living plant) and soak up food and water.

Stems vary greatly in size, appearance, and structure. (*See* STEM.) Most stems are aerial—they grow above the ground. The stems of woody plants include large amounts of woody xylem tissue. The stems of herbaceous plants are usually green and fairly weak. They include little woody xylem tissue. In general, aerial stems hold up the branches, leaves, and flowers. They also carry food, water, and minerals between the roots and other plant structures. Some stems are subterranean—they grow below the ground. Many subterranean stems have special storage or rootlike structures such as bulbs, corms, rhizomes, and tubers. Most stems have buds which make leaves, branches, or flowers. The bud at the end of a stem is called the terminal bud. It controls the letting out of plant hormones that regulate growth. Buds along the sides of the stem are called lateral buds. Each lateral bud forms at a place on the stem called a node. Flowers sometimes grow just above the node, in the axil. Many stems have tiny openings called lenticels. The lenticels let gases pass into and out of the stem.

Leaves also show great variety in size and shape. (*See* LEAF.) Most of the photosynthesis takes place in the leaves. Most leaves are green because they include large amounts of chlorophyll. Carbon dioxide enters the leaf and oxygen leaves the leaf through special openings called stomata. Since sunlight is also needed for photosynthesis, the leaves are arranged on the stem so that each leaf gets the most sunlight possible. Some leaves are large and fleshy, storing food and water. Some plants have leaves that have developed into needles, spines, or thorns. Some plants, such as deciduous trees, lose their leaves every year. Other plants, such as evergreens, may have leaves year-round.

The flower is the reproductive structure of an angiosperm. (*See* FLOWER.) Most flowers have four parts: the calyx (sepals), the corolla (petals), the stamens (pollen-producing male structures), and the pistils (ovule-producing female structures). Although some of these parts may be missing, every flower must have at least one stamen or one pistil. If a flower has only stamens, it is a male flower, and is called staminate. If a flower has only pistils, it is a female flower, and is called pistillate. Some plants have either staminate flowers or pistillate flowers, but not both. (*See* DIOECIOUS.) Some plants have both staminate

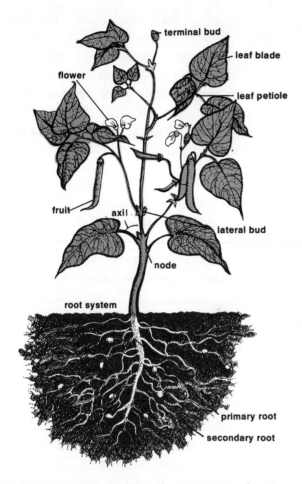

The illustration above shows the structure and parts of a typical flowering plant. Flowering plants have vegetative structures—roots, stem, and leaves—and reproductive structures—flowers, fruits, and seeds. Roots hold the plant in the ground and soak up water and minerals.

Fossil remains of plants are the only indication of what the original plants looked like. During the Carboniferous period the leafy shoots of this lycopod probably became buried in silt, which was then compressed and hardened into rock. A cast of the original plant was left when the tissues decayed, showing clearly the arrangement of the leaves on the branches.

flowers and pistillate flowers on the same plant. (*See* MONOECIOUS.)

Fertilization of an ovule takes place in the ovary of the pistil. (*See* POLLINATION.) The ovary then grows into a fruit, and the fertilized ovules develop into seeds. (*See* FRUIT; SEED.) The major work of the fruit is to help scatter the seeds of the plant. (*See* DISPERSION OF PLANTS.) It is possible for each normal seed to germinate and develop into a new plant.

Plant evolution and adaptation Scientists believe that the first plants were algaelike and lived in the oceans about four billion years ago during the Precambrian time. (*See* EVOLUTION.) The first land plants were probably the primitive psilophytes. They probably evolved from the algaelike plants about 435 million years ago during the Paleozoic era. As the Paleozoic era was drawing to a close, about 340 million years ago, there were forests of club mosses, horsetails, and ferns. Many of these plants were later formed into coal, petroleum, and natural gas. By the beginning of the Mesozoic era, about 225 million years ago when dinosaurs roamed the earth, gymnosperms had become the most widespread of the land plants. Near the end of the Mesozoic era, angiosperms had evolved.

By the beginning of the Cenozoic era, about 65 million years ago, angiosperms lived throughout the world.

As evolution continued, many plants developed lifestyles or special structures to help them grow and reproduce. Some plants grow, reproduce, and die in one year. (*See* ANNUAL PLANT.) Some plants grow for one year, then reproduce and die in the second year. (*See* BIENNIAL PLANT.) Many plants live for more than two years, usually reproducing every year. (*See* PERENNIAL PLANT.) Some plants have developed structures to protect them from being eaten by animals. In some of these plants, the leaves have been modified (changed) as spines or thorns for protection. In others, the plant has a bad tasting or poisonous fluid in the roots, stems, leaves, flowers, or fruits.

Many plants have evolved special structures to help them get or store food. Bulbs, corms, tubers, fleshy stems, and fleshy leaves are all food-storing structures. Some plants have haustoria, specialized roots that grow into a host and soak up food and water. Some plants have even evolved special structures for catching insects so that the plants may get the minerals they need. (*See* CARNIVOROUS PLANT.) Other plants have developed a lifestyle in which they live symbiotically with other organisms. (*See* SYMBIOSIS.)

Uses of plants Plants are the most important living things on earth. Without plants, there would be no other forms of life. Plants are the main source of oxygen in the air. It is believed that plants gave all the oxygen during the earth's early development. Plants also keep the carbon dioxide and oxygen levels in the air fairly well balanced.

Plants are the source of all food needed by animals. They are vital links in the food chain. (*See* FOOD CHAIN.) Plants are important in practically every cycle in nature— carbon cycle, nitrogen cycle, oxygen cycle, and so forth. They are also important in the protection of wildlife, soil, water, and other natural resources. Plants provide lumber for construction, fibers for clothing, chemicals for medicines and drugs, and hundreds of other substances which have become common parts of everyday life. *See also* ASEXUAL REPRODUCTION; BOTANY; ECOLOGY; REPRODUCTION; VEGETATIVE PROPAGATION.

A.J.C./M.H.S.

PLASMA (plaz′ mə) Plasma is the straw-colored liquid part of the blood that holds the hard parts of blood—red and white cells and platelets. Plasma is made of water, salt, proteins, and other materials.

Plasma carries food, which has been turned into liquid, or dissolved, to all parts of the body. It picks up waste material from body cells and carries it to organs that take away waste from the body.

One of the proteins found in plasma is fibrinogen. If it were not for fibrinogen, a person would bleed to death from the smallest cut. Fibrinogen makes it possible for the blood to clot (thicken and lump together) and seal off a wound. Globulin is another protein in plasma. It carries disease-fighting substances called antibodies. Antibodies kill germs and help keep disease from happening. Most antibodies are found in a portion of the globulin protein called gamma globulin. A third protein found in plasma is albumin. It helps keep the blood pressure and blood volume normal, or as they should be.

During the 1930s, researchers found that plasma could be separated from whole blood by using a machine called a centrifuge. After plasma has been separated from whole blood it can be dried or frozen and will keep for any length of time.

Plasma is used in blood transfusions (blood from one person is given to another person) to put back blood that is lost because of heavy bleeding. *See also* BLOOD; BLOOD TRANSFUSION; PROTEIN; SHOCK.

W.R.P./J.J.F.

PLASMA (PHYSICS) (plaz′ mə) Plasma is a fourth state of matter. Solids, liquids, and gases are called states of matter. If a solid is heated, it melts and turns into a liquid. At a higher temperature, the liquid boils to form a gas. The fourth state of matter, plasma, is made by heating a gas to above 50,000°C [90,000°F].

All atoms have small particles called electrons. (*See* ATOM.) In a plasma, some of the electrons are divided from the atoms. This is called ionization. When an atom loses (or gains) an electron, it is called an ion. (*See* IONS AND IONIZATION.) Plasmas can also be made by passing electricity through a gas at a very low pressure.

Plasmas usually give off light. The light comes mostly from the electrons and the ions having contact, or touching. Lightning, arc-lamps, and fluorescent lamps are all examples of plasmas. The Van Allen belts around the earth and the corona around the sun are also plasmas. Plasmas are good carriers of electricity. They are strongly affected by magnetic fields. Physicists use magnetic fields to hold plasmas at high temperatures. (*See* THERMONUCLEAR ENERGY.) *See also* MATTER; STATES OF MATTER.   M.E./J.T.

PLASMODIUM (plaz mōd′ ē əm) Plasmodium is a shapeless mass of protoplasm that has many nuclei, but lacks a firm cell wall. (*See* PROTOPLASM.) It moves by "oozing" from one place to another in what is called ameboid movement. Plasmodium is the normal body form of slime molds and some fungi. (*See* SLIME MOLD.)

Plasmodium is also a genus of malaria-causing protozoans. These one-celled animals are carried by the female *Anopheles* mosquito. (*See* MOSQUITO.) These protozoans invade the red blood cells of mammals, birds, and reptiles. When they reproduce, they destroy the blood cell, releasing toxins (poisons) and 12 to 24 new organisms. This process is repeated every 48 or 72 hours, accounting for the periodic chills and fever associated with malaria. (*See* MALARIA.) *See also* PROTOZOA.
          A.J.C./C.R.N.

PLASTER OF PARIS (plas′ tər uv par′ əs) Plaster of Paris is a white powder that is a form of calcium sulfate. The formula for plaster of Paris is $CaSO_4 \cdot \frac{1}{2}H_2O$. It is made by removing water from the mineral gypsum ($CaSO_4 \cdot 2H_2O$) when the mineral is heated to 250°C [482°F]. When water is added to plaster of Paris, it sets in a few minutes to form a hard mass of gypsum. Plaster of Paris sets without any change of volume. This makes it an ideal material for casts, molds, and pottery.   J.J.A./A.D.

PLASTIC

Plastics (plas′ tik) are synthetic (made-by-people) materials. They are easily molded into shapes, usually by applying heat and pressure. Plastic objects have many different uses. In the home, plastic is used in floor tiles, non-stick cooking pans, and heat-proof surfaces in the kitchen. In the living room, there may be curtains, carpets, and light fixtures made from plastic. Drip-dry shirts, non-iron dresses, and shoes have plastic in them. Plastics are also very important in industry and medicine.

Early plastics were used in place of other materials, such as metals. Today, plastics are used because of their own special qualities. For example, plastic tubes are used in surgery for replacing arteries that are no longer working as they should. The plastic used is very inert. This means that the body will accept it and not react to it by throwing it out. No other material could be used for this. (*See* PROSTHETICS.)

Types of Plastic   There are two main groups of plastics: thermoplastics and thermosets.

This picture shows one of the many uses of plastic—a temporary inflatable building. When plastic materials first became common, they were considered revolutionary materials. In place of wood and metal, plastic was used for a wide range of objects, such as door handles, buckets, and bowls. Also, plastic materials revolutionized industry. For example, many parts of an automobile are now made from different kinds of plastic.

Examples are polyethylene and Bakelite. Bakelite, a thermoset, is hard and rigid. (*See* BAKELITE.) Rigid means that it does not bend easily. Polyethylene, a thermoplastic, is softer and more flexible—it bends more easily than Bakelite. (*See* POLYETHYLENE.) These two plastics act differently when they are heated. Bakelite resists heat. For example, a hot pan from the stove can be placed on top of Bakelite without hurting the plastic. A hot pan would melt polyethylene. Thermoplastics soften and melt at fairly low temperatures. Melting does not damage them, however, and they harden again when they are cooled. This process of melting and cooling a thermoplastic can be repeated many times.

These two types of plastic are different from each other because their molecules are arranged differently. Both types have molecules that are long chain polymers. In thermoplastics, the chains are mostly separate from each other. There is very little linkage between the chains. In thermosetting plastics, the long chain molecules are linked together to make a network of atoms. Long separate chains of atoms can slide easily over each other. This is why thermoplastics are flexible, especially when they are warmed. When thermoplastics are bent, they never completely return to their original shape. In other words, they are not very elastic. (*See* ELASTICITY.) Other polymers, the rubbers, are elastic. They are called elastomers. (*See* RUBBER.) The network of atoms in a thermoset makes it hard and rigid. When a thermoset is heated, even more linkages are made between the atoms. This is why thermosets do not melt when they are heated.

Most of the well-known plastics are thermoplastics. Besides nylon and polyethylene, they include polystyrene, polyvinyl chloride (PVC), acrylic, polyacetal, and polytetrafluoroethylene (PTFE). There are many different kinds of nylon. Nylon is used in textiles

Polyethylene plastic film makes a hygienic wrapping for these cakes at a food factory.

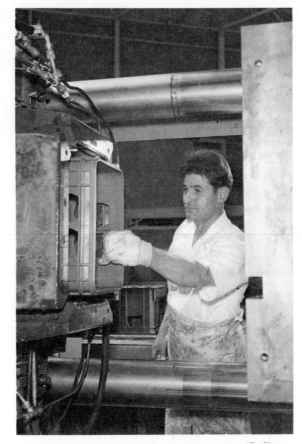

Polypropylene plastic crates can be made in less time than it takes build wooden crates.

for clothing and for making machine parts, such as gear wheels and bearings. Polyethylene, or polythene, is probably the most common plastic of all. It is used in plastic bags for wrapping food and in many household items, such as plastic buckets, bottles, and bowls. PTFE is used for coating non-stick cooking pans. It can resist heat better than any other thermoplastic. Polyacetals are tough and can also resist heat. They are used in engineering in place of the metals zinc and aluminum. Acrylic is used in fibers for clothing. The transparent plastics, Perspex and Lucite are made from acrylic. (*See* ACRYLIC.) Polystyrene is used to make many kitchen utensils. There is a type of polystyrene called expanded polystyrene. It has many tiny bubbles of air and is used in insulation and packaging. (*See* POLYSTY-RENE.) PVC is used in pipes for plumbing and also in shiny, water-resistant clothing such as coats and boots. (*See* PVC.)

Common thermosetting plastics include Bakelite, epoxy resins and urea-formaldehyde resin. Epoxy resins are used as lacquers and as strong adhesives, or glues. They are also used for coating metals and in paints that resist rusting. Bakelite is used for insulating against electricity. Casings for instruments such as radios and parts for machines are sometimes made from Bakelite. Urea-formaldehyde is similar to Bakelite. It is used for light fixtures and screw tops for bottles. Another resin is melamine-formaldehyde. It is also similar to Bakelite. Melamine-formaldehyde plastic is used in good quality plastic tableware since it does not easily stain. It is also used in heat-resistant tops for kitchen

In this photograph, rough edges are being filed off Bakelite plastic components. The components were made by injection molding.

tables. Two thermosetting plastics that are not resins are polyurethane and silicone. Polyurethane is used as a foam in upholstery. It can also be shaped to make chairs. (*See* POLYURETHANE.) Silicone is water-resistant. For this reason, it is used in polishes. (*See* SILICONES.) Some plastics can be either thermosetting or thermoplastic. An example is polyester. Thermoplastic polyester is used in fabrics. Thermosetting polyester is used to make fiberglass.

Making and shaping plastics Plastics are made by a process called polymerization. In polymerization, small molecules called monomers are linked together to make long, chainlike molecules. These long chain molecules can then be linked together or cross-linked to form a network, or system, of atoms. Hard plastics have this structure. These long molecules are called polymers. For example, polyethylene is made by linking molecules of the gas ethylene. In most types of plastics, the polymer has a "backbone" of carbon atoms. Each carbon atom is linked to two others, one on either side. The carbon atoms also have two atoms or groups of atoms joined on. Different atoms or groups of atoms make different plastics. (*See* POLYMERIZATION.)

Some polymers are natural materials. For example, protein, starch, and cellulose are natural polymers. Celluloid was the first plastic that was made. It is made by treating cellulose with a mixture of sulfuric and nitric acids. Most plastics, however, do not start from natural polymers. Most plastics are synthetics—made by people rather than nature. For polymerization to happen, a catalyst

Behind the tractor in this picture, early vegetables are growing under polyethylene plastic frames. Polyethylene is less expensive than glass, is more easily handled, and transmits almost as much light and heat as glass does.

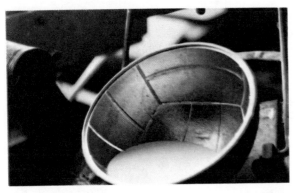

A half mold for a soccer ball is pictured. Plastic paste is inside the mold.

is needed in the reaction. A catalyst makes the reaction go at a faster rate. (*See* CATALYST.) To make a thermosetting plastic, the chain molecules have to be linked together. This is done by a process called setting or curing. This, too, often needs a catalyst.

In order to make plastic articles, the plastic has to be shaped. The most common way of doing this is by molding. Different processes are used for thermosets and thermoplastics. Objects made of thermosetting plastic are produced by compression molding. In this process, plastic pellets are placed in the bottom half of a hot mold. The top half of the mold is moved down on top of the bottom half with a great deal of pressure. This melts the plastic, causing it to flow into the shape of the mold. Under these conditions of high pressure

and temperature, the molecules link up, and the plastic sets, or molds.

Thermoplastics are much easier to shape than thermosets. This is because thermoplastics can be kept molten (melted) for a long time. There are several different methods of molding thermoplastics. A very common method is called injection molding. Plastic pellets are melted in a heated chamber. A piston then forces the molten plastic through a nozzle into a mold that is kept cool. The plastic cools and sets in the shape of the mold. The mold then opens automatically and the object is taken out of the mold.

Another method is called blow molding. Molten plastic is placed inside a mold. The mold is kept cool by water. Air is then blown into the plastic to force it into the right shape. This method is used for making plastic bottles and other hollow articles.

Another common method for shaping plastic is called extrusion. In this method, molten plastic is forced through a hole in the shape of the object to be made. For example, a circular hole is used for making rods and a slit for making films. Synthetic fibers are made this way. Molten plastic is forced through very tiny holes in a special device called spinneret. (*See* FIBER.) This method is used for nylon and polyester. (*See* EXTRUSION.)

The heat-resistant counter tops used in kitchens are made by a different process called laminating. Layers of cloth or paper are soaked in a resin such as urea-formaldehyde. The resin makes the structure strong and

Map labels: Philippine plate, San Andreas fault, North American plate, Eurasian plate, Caribbean plate, Arabian plate, Pacific plate, Cocos plate, African plate, East African rift valley, Bismark plate, Solomon's plate, Fiji plate, Nazca plate, Australian plate, South American plate, Mid Atlantic Ridge, Antarctic plate

The map shows in red the edges of the plates that make up the earth's crust. The gray areas are the continental shelves which are parts of the continents, and the broken lines show uncertain plate edges.

PLASTIC SURGERY (plas' tik sərj' ə rē) Plastic surgery is the surgical repair or rebuilding of body tissues. (*See* SURGERY.) Plastic surgeons treat physical defects (something that is wrong with the body) that existed when a person was born (congenital defects) or were caused by injury or disease. Often, the body part that is badly made or damaged does not work as it should. In such cases, the surgeon does reconstructive plastic surgery. This often requires grafting. In grafting, skin muscle, bone, or cartilage is transplanted from a healthy part of the body to the part that is hurt or damaged. Sometimes, reconstructive surgery involves reattaching severed limbs, rebuilding damaged tissues, or restoring damaged blood vessels and nerves.

People who want to make their appearance better sometimes use cosmetic plastic surgery. The most common types of cosmetic surgery are a face lift to take away wrinkles from the face and neck and a rhinoplasty to change the shape of the nose. *See also* TRANSPLANTATION. A.J.C./J.J.F.

rigid. The layers are then clamped in a press and heated to set the resin. M.E./J.M.

PLATE TECTONICS (plāt' tek tän' iks) Plate tectonics is the theory that the earth's shell, or lithosphere, is broken up into moving plates (big, movable, flat pieces of rock). Some of these plates include continents, while others include both continents and oceans. The movement and interaction of these plates is likely to be the cause of continental drift, which is believed to be the slow movement of the continents within the earth; volcanoes; mountain building; and earthquakes.

The San Andreas Fault in California is where the North American plate meets the Pacific plate. The area around this fault is very likely to have earthquakes. (*See* EARTHQUAKE; FAULT.)

Convection currents are forces beneath the earth's crust that carry molten (melted) material from the inside of the earth to the surface. Convection currents may be the cause of the Mid-Atlantic ridge. Along this ridge, new rock is always being formed from the molten material. The new rock forces the two plates to spread apart. Scientists think that this tectonic activity is slowly moving the American continents away from Europe and Africa. Ridge areas are very likely to have volcanoes. (*See* VOLCANO.)

Tectonic activity is the most likely explanation for the formation of the Himalaya Mountains. (*See* MOUNTAIN.) The plate carrying the Indian peninsula supposedly moved into the Asian plate and caused the Himalayas to rise up.

The plate tectonic theory has been accepted by almost all geologists. Those who do not accept the idea do not believe convection currents are strong enough to move continents. However, the plate tectonic theory does provide an explanation for many of the unusual geological events that have happened during the last several billion years. *See also* CONTINENTAL DRIFT; EARTH. J.M.C./W.R.S.

PLATINUM (plat′ nəm) Platinum (Pt) is a rare, silvery metallic element. Its atomic number is 78 and its atomic weight is 195.09. Platinum melts at 1,772°C [3,222°F] and boils at about 3,800°C [6,900°F]. Its relative density is 21.5.

Platinum has been known in South America since ancient times. It is found as

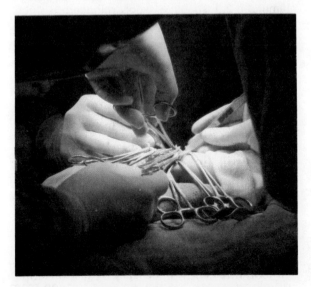

Platinum is used in manufacturing surgical instruments.

grains or nuggets in igneous rocks. It is a hard metal and is resistant (not hurt by) to heat and many chemicals. For these reasons it is used to make surgical instruments, chemical equipment, and electrodes. (*See* ELECTRODE.) It is also easily shaped into a new form. Platinum is an important catalyst. A catalyst is a substance that can speed up a chemical reaction. (*See* CATALYST.) Platinum is used in a number of different alloys. An alloy is a mixture of different metals. (*See* ALLOY.) Alloys of platinum and silver are used in dentistry. Alloys of platinum with the metal iridium are used for making electrical parts and bearings. Platinum's resistance to heat allows it to be used as a coating in nose cones of missiles and in fuel nozzles for jet engines.

M.E./J.R.W.

PLATYHELMINTHES (plat′ i hel′ minthz′) Platyhelminthes is the name of the phylum that includes a large class of free-living flatworms and two classes of parasitic flatworms, the flukes and the tapeworms. These invertebrate animals have soft, flat bodies. They have no true skeleton, respiratory system, or circulatory system. The platyhelminthes have primitive nervous and excretory systems—these systems have not changed very much since the animal first existed. Most have digestive systems with a single opening. Probably the most common non-parasitic flatworms are the freshwater planarians. *See also* BILHARZIA; INVERTEBRATE; PARASITE; TAPEWORM.

S.R.G./C.S.H.

PLATYPUS (plat′ i pəs) The platypus, or duckbill, (*Ornithorhynchus anatinus*) is a primitive mammal found in parts of Australia and the island of Tasmania. The animal is often called a duckbill because it has a bill like a duck. The bill is at the front part of the head where most mammals have noses and lips. The platypus uses its bill to hunt for shellfish, worms, and various insects on the bottom of streams. Adult platypuses have no teeth. After they lose their deciduous, or milk teeth, they use the horny plates on their upper and lower jaws to chew food.

The platypus is about 61 cm [2 ft] long, not including the tail. The tail, which is 15 cm [6 in] long, is shaped like a paddle. It helps the animal swim.

Although it lays eggs instead of bearing its young alive, the platypus is a true mammal. (*See* MONOTREME.) Like other mammals, the platypus nurses its young—feeds them with milk from its breast. The female usually has from one to three eggs. When they are hatched, she uses her tail to hold the young close to her body while nursing them.

Platypuses were once killed in great numbers for their thick, soft fur. Hunting platypuses is now against the law in Australia.

J.J.A./J.J.M.

PLEISTOCENE EPOCH (plī′ stə sēn′ ep′ ək)

The Pleistocene epoch is the division of the Quaternary period that began 2.5 million years ago and ended about 10,000 years ago. Modern humanity emerged during the Pleistocene epoch.

The Pleistocene epoch was marked by four or five ice ages—periods of time when much of the earth was covered with ice—in the northern hemisphere. During the ice ages, there was less water in the ocean than usual because of the large amount of frozen water in the glaciers (large bodies of ice). Land bridges (bridges formed by land over a body of water), such as the Bering Strait, were uncovered. This may have given animals and people the chance to move into the western hemisphere. When the glaciers left, the landscape of the northern land areas was changed. (*See* GLACIATION.)

Most modern mammals appeared during this epoch. Huge mammals like the mammoths, mastodons, and woolly rhinoceroses became extinct (no longer existed) toward the end of the Pleistocene epoch. The areas that

mammals lived in were quite different at this time. Hippopotamuses and lions lived in the British Isles and elephants lived in the southwestern United States. The reason for the extinction of large mammals at the end of the Pleistocene epoch has still not been decided. *See also* EVOLUTION; GEOLOGICAL TIME SCALE; QUATERNARY PERIOD. J.M.C./W.R.S.

Some large mammals that lived in the Pleistocene epoch are shown above. They are as follows: 1. mammoth; 2. Irish elk; 3. wooly rhinoceros, which inhabited Europe; 4. Megatherium, or giant sloth; 5. Glypotodon, a giant armadillo; and 6. Smilodon, a saber-toothed cat.

PLIMSOLL LINE (plim′ səl līn′)

The Plimsoll line is a mark on the side of a ship which shows how low in the water the ship can safely sit when it is fully loaded. If the Plimsoll line is below the water level, underneath the water, the ship is too full. A ship that is too full may sink in stormy seas.

The Plimsoll line is named after the British politician Samuel Plimsoll, who helped improve the laws for ship safety. A Plimsoll line is now necessary by law on ships of all nations. It is sometimes called the International Load Line. J.M.C./R.W.L.

PLIOCENE EPOCH (plī′ ə sēn′ ep′ ək) The Pliocene epoch, the last division of the Tertiary period, began about 7 million years ago and lasted about 4.5 million years. The Pliocene is the shortest epoch of the Tertiary period.

The Pliocene environment (conditions, such as climate, that surround and affect something) was cooler and drier than the previous epochs. Pliocene mammals began to grow to a larger size. There were many camels and horses, which were bigger than they are today. Mastodons (elephantlike mammals) began to change form so that they could live in the new environment. Primates (humanlike mammals) were developing. Some of these primates may have walked upright, such as an ape walking on two legs. The rhinoceroses of North America became extinct (no longer existed). Pliocene sea life was quite similar to that of today. During the Pliocene epoch, the Alps and the Himalayan Mountains were rising. *See also* GEOLOGICAL TIME SCALE; TERTIARY PERIOD.

J.M.C./W.R.S.

PLOVER (plʌv′ ər) A plover is a shorebird that belongs to the family Charadriidae. It has a short, straight bill; a short tail; and long, pointed wings. Many plovers walk along the shoreline, feeding on insects and small water animals. They also feed in grasslands.

There are ten species of plovers in North America. One of the most common plovers is the killdeer. It grows to about 20 cm [8 in] long. Killdeer have brown wings, white bellies, and two black bands around their necks. All plovers are strong fliers. The American golden plover, a bird about the size of a robin, spends the summer in the Arctic but flies to southern South America for the winter. This is one of the longest bird migrations known. *See also* BIRD; MIGRATION. S.R.G./L.L.S.

PLUM (pləm′) The plum is a fruit-bearing tree belonging to the Rose family, Rosaceae.

Its fruit, which can be as large as a peach, is round or oval and contains a stonelike seed. The thin skin may be purple, blue, red, yellow, or green. The flesh of the plum can be eaten fresh. The plum tree, which grows in temperate regions (mild climates) around the world, can be low and shrubby or grow to 9 m [30 ft] high.

Almost 2,000 varieties of plum are known, but only about 150 are important. The five most common plums are the European, Japanese, American, damson, and ornamental. Some of these varieties are used to make jellies, jams, and plum butter. Dried plums are known as prunes. Prunes have a high sugar content.

In the United States, most plums and prunes are grown in California. Oregon, Washington, Idaho, and Michigan are other states where plums are grown for market.

W.R.P./F.W.S.

A plum is pictured above.

PLUTO (plüt′ ō) Pluto is the ninth planet, in distance from the sun, in the solar system. Percival Lowell, an American astronomer, believed there was a planet beyond Neptune. He based his belief on Neptune's unusual orbit. In 1930 Pluto was discovered by Clyde Tombaugh, an assistant to Lowell. Pluto cannot be seen without a strong telescope.

Pluto is the smallest planet—even though many writings list Mercury as smaller. Pluto's diameter is between 2,400 and 2,900 km [1,500 and 1,800 mi]. Pluto is about 5.91 billion km [3.67 billion mi] away from the sun. Pluto takes a little less than 248 years to make a full orbit around the sun. At some points in its orbit around the sun, Pluto is closer to the sun than Neptune. Pluto takes 6.4 earth-days to make a full spin on its axis.

Very little is known about the surface of Pluto. Its tiny size and great distance from the earth make Pluto the hardest planet for astronomers to study. Pluto is probably not solid rock, and it is not likely that it has an atmosphere (air, we know it). Scientists believe that the average temperature of Pluto is below −184°C [−300°F]. This low temperature would cause most of the gases on Pluto to be frozen or at least liquefied. Life on Pluto is very unlikely. (*See* EXOBIOLOGY.)

Until 1978, Pluto was thought to have no natural satellites. However, on June 22, 1978 James W. Christy, an American astronomer, discovered that Pluto had a moon. Christy dubbed the moon Charon after his wife Charlene. Charon has a diameter of about 800 to 965 km [500 to 600 mi]. It orbits Pluto every 6.4 earth-days, the same time it takes Pluto to make a complete spin on its axis. This type of synchronized (happening at the same time) movement does not happen anywhere else in the solar system. Charon is about 19,300 km [12,000 mi] above the surface of Pluto. *See also* PLANET.

J.M.C./C.R.

PLUTONIUM (plü tō′ nē əm) Plutonium (Pu) is a radioactive metallic element. Its

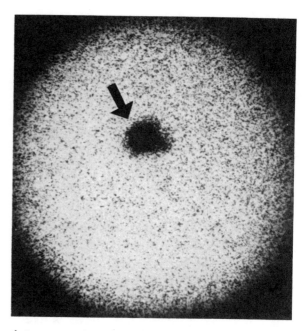

Astronomer James W. Christy discovered a moon orbiting the planet Pluto on June 22, 1978. The "bump" (see arrow) on several photos taken during observation turned out to be a moon.

1930. MARCH. 2ᴅ. 4ʜ. 56ᴍ.

1930. MARCH. 5ᴅ. 3ʜ. 44ᴍ.

Telescopic photographs made in 1930, shortly after the discovery of Pluto, are shown above. Two different positions of Pluto, shown by the arrows, indicate that Pluto is a planet and not a star.

atomic number is 94. It melts at 641°C [1,186°F] and boils at 3,232°C [5,850°F]. Its relative density is 19.8.

Plutonium is the only transuranic element that occurs naturally. But before this was discovered, in 1940 an American team of scientists headed by Edwin MacMillan made the element artificially. Fifteen isotopes of plutonium have been discovered. (*See* ISOTOPE.) The longest-lasting isotope is plutonium-239. It takes 24,400 years for half of this isotope to decay. It is used as a fuel in some nuclear reactors (*see* NUCLEAR POWER), as well in nuclear weapons. Plutonium-238 was used as a power source for equipment placed on the moon during the Apollo lunar missions.

Because the isotopes are so extremely toxic and radioactive, disposal of waste products from nuclear reactors poses grave problems.   M.E./J.R.W.

PNEUMATICS (nù mat′ iks)
Pneumatics is the branch of mechanics that deals with the behavior of compressed gases. In the seventeenth century, Torricelli studied the effects of atmospheric pressure. As a result of Torricelli's work, practical air pumps that could compress (press together) air were built. Modern pneumatic devices that work with compressed air include riveting hammers, road drills or jackhammers, sandblasting equipment, auto garage tools, and dental drills. Compressed air is also used in some vehicle braking systems, and to fill vehicle tires.   W.R.P./J.T.

PNEUMATOPHORE (nù mat′ ə fōr′)
Pneumatophores are breathing tubes produced by mangrove trees and some other plants that grow in water. The roots of mangroves grow in mud below the water. They get air for respiration (breathing) from tubes that grow above the top of the water. The tubes, which are open to the air at the top, are filled with spongy tissue that has a number of holes joined together. The air passes through these holes to the roots. *See also* MANGROVE.

W.R.P./M.H.S.

PNEUMONIA (nù mō′ nyə)
Pneumonia is a lung disease that is usually caused by a microorganism (bacterium, fungus, virus). It may also be caused by exposure to radiation or by breathing in chemical fumes or powders. Pneumonia causes the alveoli (air sacs) of the lungs to become irritated. When this happens, the body pours fluids and white blood cells into the alveoli to fight the infection. (*See* ANTIBODY.) The symptoms of pneumonia include chills, fever, chest pain, coughing, and difficulty in breathing. Frequently, the diseased person coughs up rust-colored phlegm—mucus that contains blood from the irritated lung tissues. The symptoms usually last for a week to ten days until the body's defenses begin to control the disease. Antibiotics greatly lessened the number of deaths due to pneumonia. (*See* ANTIBIOTIC.)

Pneumonia is most commonly caused by the *pneumococcus* bacterium. (*See* BACTERIA.) Pneumococci is present in the bodies of many healthy persons. If the body becomes weakened because of sickness, colds, surgery, or exhaustion, the pneumococci can quickly upset the body's defenses and cause pneumonia. Another bacterium, *mycoplasma*, also causes pneumonia. The body develops an immunity to this bacterium, so it does not usually affect the same person more than once. (*See* IMMUNITY.) Viral and bacterial pneumonia are very contagious. The microorganisms become airborne when a person who has pneumonia coughs, sneezes, or spits. As a result, pneumonia can quickly become epidemic. (*See* EPIDEMIC.)

Pneumonia is often named for the structures it includes. Lobar pneumonia affects one or more lobes of the lung. Double pneumonia is lobar pneumonia in both lungs.

Bronchopneumonia affects the bronchi and bronchioles, the tubes leading to the lungs. Pneumonia is a serious disease that should always be treated by a doctor. The patient should get plenty of rest, fluids, and fresh air. In addition, he, or she, should avoid crowds and contact with other people. *See also* LUNG; MICROORGANISM; VIRUS.   A.J.C./J.J.F.

POD (päd′) A pod is another name for a legume, and is commonly used to describe the fruits of members of the pea family. *See also* FRUIT; LEGUME.   A.J.C./M.H.S.

POISON (poiz′ ən) A poison is a substance that causes irritation (soreness, roughness or redness on part of the body), injury, sickness, and possibly death.

Corrosive poisons—poisons that slowly eat away at something—kill living tissue. A person who swallows this type of poison may hurt the lining of the mouth or throat. Sodium hydroxide is an example of a corrosive poison. (*See* LYE.)

Irritant poisons cause swelling and soreness of the mucous membranes. (*See* INFLAMMATION.) Mucous membranes line many air passages of the body, such as the nose. Irritant poisons may also hurt the stomach, intestines, and nerve centers.

Systematic poisons attack the nervous system and other important organs, such as the liver and heart. For example, strychnine causes convulsions (unusual muscle movement) and makes it hard for a person to swallow. Many barbituates, taken in large doses, are systematic poisons. (*See* BARBITUATE.)

Poisonous gases make it hard for a person to breathe and can sometimes cause death. Some gases irritate the eyes, nose, or skin. Carbon monoxide is a very dangerous poisonous gas because it is hard to notice at first. (*See* CARBON MONOXIDE.)

Food poisoning can come from eating certain chemicals or organisms and their toxins (poisons). For example, chemicals such as insecticides can cause food poisoning. (*See* INSECTICIDE.) When organisms make a poison, the poison is called a toxin. The study of poisons is called toxicology. Organisms such as hemlock and certain shellfish can also cause food poisoning. Botulism is a poisoning caused by a toxin made by bacteria. Botulism can cause paralysis and death. (*See* BOTULISM.)

There are many treatments for poisoning. It is always best to call a physician as soon as possible because the way to treat one type of poisoning may not be the best way to treat another type of poisoning.

The strongest poisons are not usually found in everyday surroundings. Most poisoning is caused by weaker poisons that are included in many household products. In the United States, about two million people become sick from poisoning each year.

J.J.A./J.J.F.

POISONOUS PLANT (poiz′ nəs plant′) There are about 700 species of poisonous plants in the United States and Canada. Some are harmful only if they are eaten. Others spread poisons by touching the leaves or other structures. Some give off pollen or other substances which may cause an allergic reaction in certain people. (*See* ALLERGY.) In some poisonous plants, the whole plant is harmful, while in others, only parts of the plant are poisonous. For example, the stalks of rhubarb (*Rheum rhaponticum*) are a popular vegetable. The leaves, however, are poisonous. (*See* RHUBARB.)

Many poisonous plants have a bad taste or smell, and it is easy to keep away from them. Others, though, are very pretty and are often grown as decorative plants. The mountain laurel (*Kalmia latifolia*), for example, makes beautiful pink or white flowers. It is the state flower of Connecticut and Pennsylvania. It is

The aril (facing right) of the yew tree has an attractive appearance, but is also poisonous.

also poisonous.

The most deadly of the poisonous plants is the rosary pea (*Abrus precatorius*). It is often used as a bead in making bracelets or rosary beads. One seed from this plant can, if eaten, kill an adult. Many kinds of mushrooms are also poisonous. (*See* MUSHROOM.) Oleander (*Nerium oleander*) has been known to kill people who used it as a stick to hold meat that was being cooked over a fire. The poison passed from the stick into the meat. Although many plant families have poisonous species, the main ones are the crowfoot, nightshade, and spurge families. Many of the poisons in these plants are alkaloids. (*See* ALKALOID.) Frequently, these poisons are very useful as medicines if they are used in small amounts.

Poison ivy (*Rhus radicans*) is a woody vine or shrub that is common in North America, especially in the northeastern United States. Its leaves are made of three notched leaflets. Two of these leaflets form an opposite pair near the end of a stem, and the third is at the end of that stem. The leaves are usually red in the spring, shiny green in the summer, and reddish-orange in the fall. Small greenish flowers grow in the axils and make poisonous, berrylike fruits that are usually yellow in color. The leaves make an oil which sticks to the skin or clothing. If this oil is not washed off the skin within an hour or two after touching the plant, it is taken into the skin. It causes a bad, itchy inflammation (redness and soreness) of the skin that may last for more than two weeks. If poison ivy is burned, the smoke includes the poisonous oil. If the smoke is breathed in, it will cause serious irritation (soreness) of the lungs. The best protection against poison ivy is knowing what it looks like and staying away from it. (*See* SUMAC.) *See also* POISON.　　A.J.C./M.H.S.

POLAR BEAR (pō′ lər baər′) The polar bear (*Ursus maritimus* or *Thalarctos*) is a large, white species of bear living in cold Arctic regions such as Alaska, Canada, Green-land, and Siberia. (*See* BEAR.) Some bears have traveled as far south as the Gulf of St. Lawrence, about 1,200 km [720 mi] south of the Arctic Circle. The polar bear may grow as tall as 2.5 m [8.25 ft], and weigh as much as 455 kg [1000 lb]. It has thick, white fur which is used both as camouflage and as protection from the cold. (*See* CAMOUFLAGE.) It also has a thick layer of fat to keep it warm and to help it float. The head of the polar bear is small in comparison to its long neck. These features help the bear swim quickly—5 to 10 km [3 to 6 mi] per hour. The polar bear has pads of hair on its feet. This hair helps the bear walk on ice and protects its feet from the cold.

The polar bear is a very good hunter. It can spot prey (something that is to be killed for food) from a great distance. It is able to run fast enough—40 km [25 mi] per hour—to catch up with and kill most prey. Unlike other bears, the polar bear almost always eats meat. Its diet is made up of seals, walruses, fish, and any dead sea animals that may be washed ashore. When there is not enough food during the winter, the bear may hunt and attack human beings in its search for food.

The pregnant female polar bear digs a den in the snow to protect herself and sleeps during the winter. In March or April, the mother gives birth to one or two cubs. By the end of the summer, these cubs can take care of themselves in most ways. However, before they are independent, the mother is very protective

Polar bears are popular animals in zoos, but in the wild, they are extremely dangerous.

and will try to kill anyone or anything that she thinks might hurt her cubs.

Polar bears have been hunted for their meat, hides (skins), and bones. By the early 1970s, they were declared an endangered species—a species in danger of becoming extinct. The United States, Canada, Russia, and other countries have agreed to not allow the hunting of polar bears.   A.J.C./J.J.M.

POLARIS *See* NORTH STAR.

POLARIZED LIGHT (pō′ lə rīzd′ līt′) Polarized light is waves of light that vibrate in one plane and direction only, unlike ordinary sunlight which vibrates in all planes. In the sea, waves move across the surface of the water. However, the water just bobs up and down as the wave moves over it. The water does not move forward or backward. The water moves at right angles to the direction that the wave travels—if the waves are moving in a straight line across and the water is moving in a straight line up-and-down, the two lines meeting make a right angle. This kind of wave motion is called transverse wave motion. Light is also a transverse wave motion. It vibrates (moves from side to side) in a plane (an imaginary flat surface) at right angles to its direction of motion. Usually the vibrations are in any direction in that plane. However, sometimes the light vibrates in one direction only. It is then called plane or linearly polarized light.

Plane polarized light can be made in several different ways. When light hits glass, part of it is reflected (thrown off) and part of it goes into the glass. The light that goes into the glass is bent through an angle. This is called refraction. (*See* REFRACTION OF LIGHT). The ray that goes into the glass is called the refracted ray. If the reflected and refracted rays are at right angles to each other, then the reflected ray is plane polarized.

Certain materials polarize light that passes through them. An example is Polaroid plastic sheet. Polaroid lets through only light that vibrates in a certain direction. Because of this, the light is polarized when it leaves Polaroid. Polaroid sheet is used in sunglasses to lessen the glare of the sun, and in camera filters to make clouds stand out clearly against the sky.

Plane polarized light is also made by a device called a Nicol prism. A Nicol prism is made of two pieces of a transparent (clear) mineral called calcite. They are joined together by a substance called Canada balsam. When light goes into calcite, it is split into to rays. Both of these rays are plane polarized. When they hit the layer of Canada balsam, they act in a different way. One ray is reflected by the layer of Canada balsam, but the other passes through it. The two rays are therefore separated, or divided. The ray that passes through the Canada balsam comes out as a single ray of plane polarized light. Nicol prisms are used for making polarized light in very high-quality optical instruments.

There are other kinds of polarization besides plane polarization. Sometimes the direction of light vibration moves round in a circle as the light wave moves along. This is called circular polarization. The vibration can also move in an oval shape called an ellipse. This is elliptical polarization.   M.E./S.S.B.

POLAROID CAMERA (pō′ lə roid′ kam′ ə rə) The Polaroid camera takes, prints, and develops its own photographs in a matter of minutes. This "instant" camera was invented by Edwin H. Land of the United States. The first Polaroid camera was sold in 1948. It took only black-and-white photos. Later, another model was built that could take, print, and develop color photos.

Polaroid cameras are loaded with a double picture roll. One part is a negative roll of film, and the other is a positive roll of special printing paper. Small pods (containers) of chemicals are joined to the positive roll. After exposure to light through the lens of the camera, the negative and positive rolls are made to pass through a pair of rollers that break the chemical pods. The chemicals flow over the exposed portion of the negative roll, and develop a negative image on the roll—the parts of the picture that should be black are white, and the parts that should be white are black. More chemical reactions happen between the pod chemicals and the chemicals coated on the positive roll, and a positive photograph is made—the white areas in the photo are printed white and the black areas are printed black. This process takes about 10 seconds for a black-and-white photo, and up to a minute for a color photo. Early Polaroid models needed more developing and printing time than one minute.

In 1972, Land introduced an improved "pocket model" of his camera, called the SX-70. In this camera, the photographic process is automatically controlled by tiny electronic circuits. About a second after pressing the shutter button, which opens and closes the aperture of the camera, a dry plastic square comes out of the camera. It develops quickly into a color print.

In 1978, Land introduced an instant home movie system, called "Polarvision," but it never became popular. And Polaroid has made "instant" slide film available for 35 mm cameras. *See also* CAMERA, PHOTOGRAPHY.　　　　　　　　　　W.R.P./R.W.L.

POLE (pōl′) The word pole has many scientific meanings. The two points where a planet's axis of rotation intersect (cut across and divide) the planet's surface are called poles, or geographic poles.

A celestial pole is a point in the sky around which the stars seem to circle. (*See* CELESTIAL SPHERE.)

A magnetic pole is a point where magnetic lines of force leave the magnet or the magnetically-charged object. Opposite magnetic poles (poles across from each other) attract each other, while the same magnetic

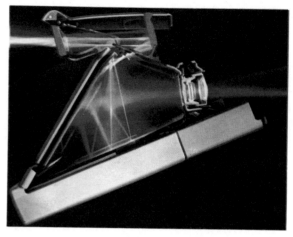

The pathway of light through a Polaroid camera is a complicated one, as shown by this model.

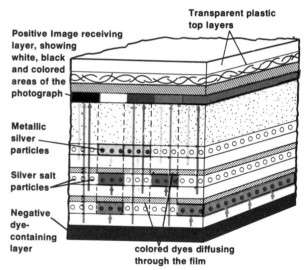

The diagram shows a section of a Polaroid film, and how it is developed while still inside the camera. When the film is exposed to light, during the taking of a photograph, particles of a silver salt in the film are reduced by light to metallic silver. After the photo has been taken, a chemical is released which dissolves dyes in the film. These dyes diffuse upward, as shown by the colored arrows. When the dyes reach parts of layers containing metallic silver particles, they become oxidized and and fixed. But the dyes continue to diffuse upward, through parts of layers where the silver salt has not been reduced to metallic silver, until they reach the image-receiving layer. White light from the photographed subject, since it contains all colors, will stop all the dyes diffusing. Areas exposed to colored light from the subject will stop some dyes, but not others, and so will appear colored in the photograph. Areas which receive no light will stop none of the dyes, but the dyes combine together to become black. Thus, the Polaroid photograph is a true positive image of the photographed subject.

poles repel (do not attract) each other. *See also* MAGNETISM.   J.M.C./C.R.

POLECAT (pōl′ kat′) The polecat (*Mustela putorius*) is a mammal belonging to the weasel family, Mustelidae. It is closely related to the North American weasel and mink. Like the mink, the polecat can discharge a nauseous odor at will.

The polecat prefers wooded country. But it does live on coastal sand dunes and open hillsides. The polecat sometimes makes its home in a hole in the ground or in a tree. The animal's main food is rabbit. It also eats rats, mice, eels, frogs, snakes, eggs, and birds.

The male polecat is about 56 cm [22 in] long, not including its tail. Female polecats are a little shorter.

Polecats have long, blackish-purple shiny fur. At one time, polecats were common throughout Europe. However, many polecats are killed because they eat some domestic food and game birds.   J.J.A./J.J.M.

POLIOMYELITIS (pō′ lē ō mī′ ə līt′ əs) Poliomyelitis, or polio, as it is commonly called, is a disease caused by a virus. In most people who are infected (catch the disease), there are no signs or symptoms. Some people may have a headache, or a sore throat, and feel as though they have a cold. In about 10 percent of patients, however, the disease becomes very serious. The virus attacks the nervous system. It kills groups of nerves in the spinal cord and sometimes damages (hurts) the brain. It attacks motor nerves (the nerves of movement) where they leave the spinal cord. Because of this, groups of muscles may become paralyzed. (*See* PARALYSIS.)

When the disease does attack the nervous system, it may affect only the spinal cord. This is called spinal polio. If the disease affects only the nerve centers of the brain, it is called bulbar polio. In its most serious form, polio affects both regions. This is spinobulbar polio.

When the spinal cord is damaged, body movements below the neck are affected. All groups of muscles are not paralyzed at one time. There may be paralysis of the arms only, of the legs only, or of just one limb (one arm or one leg). When the nerve centers of the brain are attacked, the muscles of breathing and swallowing may be paralyzed. Patients with breathing difficulties were once helped by means of the "iron lung"—a kind of artificial respirator, in which the patient was placed. Today there are better kinds of artificial respirators to help the patient breathe.

The paralysis is first noticed a week or two after a person has been infected. Usually, it does not get worse after the first two or three days. In two or three weeks, the patient begins to feel better. Further improvement continues for about eighteen months.

Patients with paralysis can be helped by physical treatment and by exercises. Paralyzed limbs may be held up by splints. Sometimes, surgery can help relieve paralysis.

Before vaccines were developed to give protection, as many as 58,000 people were affected by polio in a single year. The first polio vaccine was made by Dr. Jonas E. Salk in 1955. Later, Dr. Albert B. Sabin developed better vaccines which could be given through the mouth. These and other vaccines have been used to give immunity to most of the people in the world. (*See* IMMUNITY.) Today, fewer than 500 people a year are affected by polio. Scientists believe that in the near future, the disease will be totally controlled. *See also* NERVOUS SYSTEM; VACCINATION; VIRUS.
                                              D.M.H.W./J.J.F.

POLLEN (päl′ ən) Pollen is a yellowish powder that is made up of pollen grains, the male gametes of flowering plants and conifers. (*See* GAMETE.) The pollen grains are made in the anther of the stamen, the male part of a flower, or in pollen-bearing cones. (*See* FLOWER.) In sexual reporoduction, a pollen grain fertilizes an ovule (egg) from the

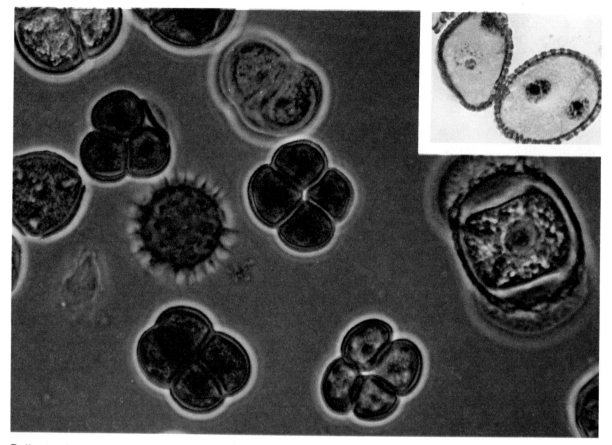

Pollen grains are many shapes and colors, as shown in the microscopic view above. The inset (top right corner) is a cross section of pollen grains, showing two nuclei. One nucleus fertilizes the egg of the female flower, and the other fertilizes the endosperm cell.

same species. The shape and structure (the way it is built or made) of pollen grains is different in each species). All the pollen grains made by any one species, however, are alike.

Pollen grains vary in size from about 0.005 to 0.25 mm [0.0002 to 0.01 in] in diameter (width). They have three layers. The layer on the outside, called exine, is very strong and is resistant to (not hurt by) many chemicals as well as to very high or low temperatures. The middle layer, called intine, is mostly cellulose. The layer on the inside, the living part of the grain, is the actual male gamete. Because of this three-layer structure, pollen grains are able to live in bad environ-

mental conditions for long periods of time. Some have been able to pollinate plants after having been stored for more than 10 years.

Since many types of pollen are scattered by the wind or insects, the grains are usually very lightweight and are made in great numbers. Some grains have been found as high as 5 km [3 mi] in the air and more than 160 km [100 mi] away from the plant that made them. A single male (staminate) flower may make more than 50 million pollen grains. Although most of these pollen grains are lost in the wind, their great numbers make it certain that some will reach and pollinate other plants, or other flowers on the same plant. (*See* POLLINATION.) Pollen grains floating in the air are the cause of many cases of hay fever. Hay fever is an allergy to airborne pollen. (*See* ALLERGY.) *See also* ANGIO-SPERM; FERTILIZATION; GYMNOSPERM.

A.J.C./M.H.S.

POLLINATION (päl′ ə nā′ shən) Pollination is the transfer of pollen (male gametes) from the male structure of a plant to the female structure of the same or a different plant. In angiosperms, pollination is the transfer of pollen from the anther of a flower to the stigma of a flower. (*See* FLOWER.) The anther is the pollen-producing part of the stamen, the male reproductive structure. The stigma is the sticky, upper part of the pistil, the female reproductive structure. Pollination is part of sexual reproduction in plants. It is usually followed by fertilization, and later by the formation (the developing and making) of a seed.

Both male gametes (pollen) and the female gametes (ovules) form by meiosis. (*See* MEIOSIS.) In the anther, meiosis causes the formation of four pollen grains from each parent cell. Each of these pollen grains is able to fertilize an ovule (egg). In the ovary of the pistil, meiosis causes the formation of one large ovule and three tiny polar bodies (cells that separate during meiosis) from each parent cell. One of these polar bodies is so small that it breaks apart almost instantly.

When a pollen grain lands on a stigma, a chemical reaction takes place. This chemical happening causes the pollen grain to form a pollen tube. The pollen tube grows through the style (a part of the plant's ovary) into the ovary where it meets an ovule and two polar bodies. As the pollen grain begins to travel down the pollen tube, its nucleus splits into two nuclei by mitosis. One nucleus fertilizes the ovule, forming an embryo, or young plant. The other nucleus joins with the two polar bodies in a process called triple fusion. Triple fusion causes the formation of an endosperm. (*See* ENDOSPERM.) The endosperm gives food for the growing embryo. Together, the embryo and endosperm make up a seed. (*See* SEED.)

There are two types of pollination: self-pollination and cross-pollination. Self-pollination is the transfer of pollen from the anther of a flower to the stigma of the same flower. Plants that normally self-pollinate usually have odorless flowers—the flowers have no smell. In many cases, self-pollination happens before the blossom even opens. Cross-pollination is the transfer of pollen from the anther of one flower to the stigma of another flower of the same species. Cross-pollination makes stronger offspring than those made by self-pollination. (*See* HYBRID.) Many plants have developed ways of helping cross-pollination or not helping self-pollination. In some plants, the anthers are below the stigmas, making self-pollination not easy. In some flowers, the stamens and pistils grow at different times. Some plants make either staminate (male) flowers or pistillate (female) flowers. (*See* DIOECIOUS.) Some plants have both staminate and pistillate flowers on one plant. (*See* MONOECIOUS.) Some plants have a chemical barrier which keeps self-pollination from happening.

Cross-pollination may be done in many ways. Most trees, shrubs, and grasses, for example, depend on the wind to carry pollen from one flower to another. Many of these wind-pollinators are odorless and do not have nectar. They usually make large amounts of very lightweight pollen. Since many of the pollen grains are lost in the wind, the large numbers help make it certain that a few will reach stigmas of other flowers.

Birds and insects are common carriers of pollination. When a bird feeds on nectar, some pollen rubs off on its body. As the bird flies from flower to flower, it spreads pollen. Some birds, such as hummingbirds, are specially suited for pollinating certain flowers. Hummingbirds have long, thin beaks which can get into tube-shaped flowers. This lets the bird feed on nectar at the base of the flower.

Insects are among the most common carriers of pollination. They may be attracted to a flower by its scent (smell) or coloring. Some flowers, such as members of the orchid family, have developed petals that look like female insects. (*See* MIMICRY.) When a male insect tries to mate with these flowers, it spreads pollen. Some flowers need a specific insect for pollination. The yucca, for example, can be pollinated only by the yucca moth (genus *Tegeticula*). Some flowers, such as some members of the honeysuckle family, open at night to attract a specific moth. (*See* NOCTURNAL HABIT.)

Pollination also happens in gymnosperms, most of which make gametes in cones. The male cone is soft and small, and makes pollen. The female cone is usually larger, and makes ovules. Pollen from the male cone is carried by the wind to the female cone where it is held by a sticky substance near the ovules. The pollen grain then grows a pollen tube in which sperm cells form. One sperm cell fertilizes an ovule which grows into a seed. The seed, when grown, falls to the ground where it can germinate (begin to grow) and make a new plant.

Scientists often use artificial methods—ways of doing something that are not from nature—to cross-pollinate plants. They carefully take away pollen from one plant and brush it on the stigma or female cone of another plant. In this way, they are able to make purebred or hybrid varieties. (*See* BREEDING.) Artificial cross-pollination is an important set of information for geneticists. It has helped geneticists add to what they know about heredity. (*See* MENDEL, GREGOR.) *See also* FERTILIZATION; GENETICS; HEREDITY; HONEYSUCKLE FAMILY; ORCHID FAMILY; POLLEN; REPRODUCTION.   A.J.C./M.H.S.

POLLUTION

Pollution (pə lü′ shən) is the contamination of the environment—air, water, and land—with harmful wastes from human activities. Environmental pollution has become a major worldwide problem. It ruins naturally beautiful scenery. It interferes with normal cycles in nature, such as the food chain, carbon cycle, nitrogen cycle, and oxygen cycle. Because there are so many complex interrelationships in the environment, a pollutant that harms one part almost always affects other parts. (*See* ECOSYSTEM.) As a result, pollution damages or destroys plant and animal life. Most importantly, though, pollution causes sickness and death among human beings.

People have always polluted the environment. When most people lived in rural areas and there were no factories or cars, pollution was not much of a problem. With the industrial revolution in the late 1700s and the growth of cities, motor vehicle use, and technology in general in the 1800s and 1900s, however, pollution became more and more important. By the mid-1900s, pollution affected almost all of the land, water, and air in the United States and other developed countries.

Recently, acid rain has come to be recognized as a form of pollution causing serious damage to the environment, particularly in the United States, Canada, and Western Europe. Sulfur and nitrogen oxides in smoke from factories, steel mills, and nonnuclear power plants react with water vapor in the air to form acids. When these acids fall to earth, in rain, they strip trees of their leaves and kill the aquatic plants that fish feed on.

Air pollution Polluted air damages plants and animals. It has also been shown to be a cause of many human illnesses such as cancer and many lung diseases. Most air pollution is caused by burning fuels to release energy. Few Americans still rely on open fires for heating and cooking. The electricity which seems so "clean" in the home is often produced by burning coal or petroleum products.

This process releases harmful gases and tiny particles—particulates—into the air. Factories and industrial plants produce large amounts of air pollution every day.

Although it is easy to blame other sources for air pollution, the major cause is the automobile. The exhaust produced by internal combustion engines contains several poisonous gases and particulates. Carbon monoxide, nitrogen dioxide, sulfur dioxide, and many other poisons are released by automobile engines. To combat automobile pollution, the federal government enacted legislation requiring that new cars be able to use unleaded fuel to reduce the amount of lead-containing poisons in the air. Pollution-control devices have been added to the engines to further reduce pollution. The exhaust, however, remains highly poisonous. In some cities, automobiles cause more than 90% of the total air pollution.

Weather also affects air pollution. Rain helps wash pollutants out of the air. Unfortunately, these pollutants remain harmful even on the ground. Sometimes, an atmospheric condition called a thermal inversion occurs. In an inversion, a layer of warm air traps a layer of cold air near the ground. This also keeps polluted air from dispersing into the upper atmosphere, resulting in dense smog. (*See* SMOG) A thermal inversion caused the 1952 London smog which killed more than 4,000 people. In the United States, Los Angeles, California, is the city most regularly affected by smog. Every year, dozens of people are hospitalized, and many die, because of the polluted air.

Water pollution Most water pollution comes from factories, farms, and homes. Chemicals, human and animal wastes, and many other substances are dumped into rivers and oceans each year. Many large cities treat sewage before it is released into a body of water. (*See* SEWAGE TREATMENT.) Even this treated sewage contains harmful pollutants, however. Bacteria and other microorganisms

Workmen are shown spraying detergent onto oil washed up on a beach in Cornwall, England.

absorb some of these wastes as part of the food chain. (*See* FOOD CHAIN.) Some of these bacteria release a gas called methane which can be used as a fuel. Sometimes, the pollutants cause an unnatural increase in the numbers of certain microorganisms. This is called eutrophication and may result in a ''dead'' body of water in which all the oxygen has been used up. (*See* SUCCESSION.) Fertilizers and phosphate-containing detergents are a major factor in this process.

Thermal pollution is caused by adding hot water to a cooler body of water. This disrupts the natural balance and kills many living organisms in the area. Thermal pollution is a major problem near nuclear power plants. (*See* NUCLEAR POWER.) In order to control nuclear reactions in these power plants, large amounts of water are heated to a high temperature. Though partially cooled, this waste water is usually much hotter than the water into which it is poured.

In the oceans, oil spills are a major source of pollution. Spills occur from accidents involving either offshore drilling rigs or the giant tanker ships that carry crude oil all over the world. Oil spills kill waterfowl and fish. The oil washes up on beaches, making them unfit for recreational use and enjoyment.

Land pollution Much land pollution is caused by the use of pesticides and other chemicals. Often, a pesticide poisons many more organisms than those for which it was intended. Some of these poisons are passed through the food chain, eventually reaching and harming human beings. (*See* INSECTICIDE.)

Strip mining, careless farming, construction, and other practices may lead to soil erosion. (*See* SOIL EROSION.) Eroded soil is useless and often leads to other troubles such as floods or famine.

Solid wastes are another major cause of land pollution. Billions of tons of solid wastes are discarded each year. Empty cans, wrappers, cars, papers, scrap metal, and many other solids end up on roadsides or in dumps. In the United States alone, more than 2.7 billion metric tons [3 billion tons] of solid wastes are produced each year. Some of these wastes decay and are said to be biodegradable. Others, such as aluminum cans and plastics, do not decay and remain as garbage forever.

Other kinds of pollution In many places, noise pollution is a major problem. Noise is produced by airplanes, cars, construction, and many other things. Radiation is another dangerous pollutant. It is invisible and is constantly hitting the earth from outer space. The most dangerous radiation, however, is produced right here on earth. Nuclear weapons, X rays, microwave ovens, and even CB radios all produce radiation which is, or may be, harmful.

Pollution control Some parts of the environment are so polluted that they may have been permanently destroyed. Much of this pollution occurred before people really knew what they were doing. As scientists, politicians, and other people have become more aware, there has been an attempt to limit future pollution and to clean up the pollution that already exists. The Environmental Protection Agency, formed in 1970, has the power to set pollution standards and to enforce them. Many state and local governments have established similar agencies to control pollution. Governments throughout the world are finally beginning to lead the fight against pollution.

There are many private groups and citizens organizations which deal with the pollution problem. Perhaps the most important pollution fighter, though, is each individual person. Although it is easy to pollute, if each person makes the effort pollution can be greatly reduced. Littering is the careless and inconsiderate disposal of solid wastes. Many solid wastes, such as aluminum cans, glass bottles, old automobile tires, and newspapers, can be recycled. When something is recycled, it is used again either in the same or different form. Some places in the United States pay people to bring in used goods for recycling. One major factor in air pollution is that many people use cars needlessly. Carpools, public transportation, bicycles, or walking are all good, pollution-preventing alternatives. *See also* CONSERVATION; ECOLOGY; ENVIRONMENT. A.J.C./R.J.B.

This picture shows sewage pollution in Lake Erie. The polluted water shows up blue in this photograph taken with infrared film.